Harold R Foster

Prince Valiant

COMPRISING PAGES 1553 THROUGH 1596

Doppelgänger

FANTAGRAPHICS BOOKS

ABOUT THIS EDITION:

Produced in cooperation with the Danish publisher Carlsen and several other publishers around the world, this new edition of PRINCE VALIANT is intended to be the definitive compilation of Hal Foster's masterpiece.

In addition to this volume, Fantagraphics Books has in stock thirty-one more collections of Foster's Prince Valiant work (Vols. 1-2 and 6-34). The ultimate goal is to have the entirety of Hal Foster's epic, comprising 40 volumes, in print at once.

ABOUT THE PUBLISHER:

FANTAGRAPHICS BOOKS has dedicated itself to bringing readers the finest in comic book and comic strip material, both new and old. Its "classics" division includes *The Complete E.C. Segar Popeye,* the *Complete Little Nemo in Slumberland* hardcover collection, and *Pogo* and *Little Orphan Annie* reprints. Its "modern" division is responsible for such works as *Love and Rockets* by Los Bros. Hernandez, Peter Bagge's *Hate,* Daniel Clowes's *Eightball,* Chris Ware's *ACME,* and American editions of work by Muñoz & Sampayo, Lewis Trondheim, and F. Solano Lopez, as well as *The Complete Crumb Comics.*

PREVIOUS VOLUMES IN THIS SERIES:

PRINCE VALIANT, Volume 35
"Doppelgänger"
comprising pages 1553 (November 13, 1966) through 1596 (September 10, 1967)
Published by Fantagraphics Books, 7563 Lake City Way NE, Seattle, WA 98115
Editorial Co-Ordinator: Henning Kure and Jens Trasborg
Colored by Jesper Ejsing
Cover inked by Mardøn Smet
Fantagraphics Books staff: Kim Thompson and Mark Vick
Copyright ©1998 King Features Syndicate, Inc., Bull's, Interpresse, & Fantagraphics Books, Inc.
Printed in Denmark
ISBN 1-56097-332-3
First Printing: Fall, 1998

Prince Valiant
IN THE DAYS OF KING ARTHUR
BY HAROLD R FOSTER

Our Story: WILD STORIES REACH CAMELOT. MERMAIDS, WATER NYMPHS AND OTHER MAGICAL CREATURES HAVE BEEN SEEN OFF THE COAST NEAR LLANTWIT. PRINCE VALIANT IS WORRIED, FOR HIS FAMILY IS ON A HOLIDAY NEAR THERE. HE ASKS KING ARTHUR FOR THE KEY TO MERLIN'S LABORATORY.

NO ONE HAS ENTERED THIS TOWER ROOM SINCE THE GREAT WIZARD DISAPPEARED, BUT VAL, A PUPIL OF MERLIN'S IN BYGONE DAYS, IS FAMILIAR WITH THE LIBRARY.

IN DUSTY TOMES AND YELLOWED SCROLLS HE FINDS MANY REFERENCES TO THESE SEAGOING LADIES AND MAKES A LONG LIST....

....APHRODITE AROSE FROM THE SEA WITH AN ESCORT OF MERMAIDS. LEDA WAS A WATER NYMPH. THEN THERE WAS THE SIREN, LORELEI; ANOTHER SIREN ALMOST OVERCAME ULYSSES. THE LADY OF THE LAKE GAVE EXCALIBUR TO ARTHUR.

VAL SETS OUT FOR LLANTWIT TAKING WITH HIM AS GUIDES THE KNIGHTS WHO CLAIMED TO HAVE SEEN THESE MYTHOLOGICAL BEINGS. IN HIS ANXIETY FOR THE SAFETY OF HIS FAMILY HE HAS FORGOTTEN MERLIN'S TEACHING.

WHEN THEY ARRIVE AT THE CLIFF'S EDGE QUITE A CROWD HAS FOLLOWED. THE SEA, SPARKLING IN THE SUNLIGHT, IS EMPTY SAVE FOR A FEW GULLS.

1553   © King Features Syndicate, Inc., 1966. World rights reserved.   11-13

"THERE SHE IS!" THEN, AS SHE GLIDES IN CLOSER, "SHE HAS A TAIL ALL COVERED WITH GOLDEN SCALES!" "NOT SO," EXCLAIMS ANOTHER. "IT IS HER GOLDEN HAIR." "LET US DRAW BACK LEST SHE BE A SIREN AND LURE US TO OUR DOOM!"

STRAIGHT FOR THE FOOT OF THE CLIFF THE CREATURE COMES. THEY CANNOT TELL IF IT BE A MERMAID, FOR HER GOLDEN HAIR FLOWS OUT BEHIND LIKE A CLOAK. THEN, BEFORE THEIR VERY EYES, SHE RETURNS TO THE DEPTHS.

NEXT WEEK- *Can Mermaids Blush?*

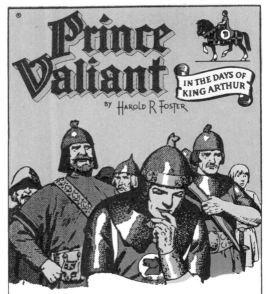

Prince Valiant
IN THE DAYS OF KING ARTHUR
BY HAROLD R. FOSTER

Our Story: IN AWED SILENCE THE GROUP ON THE CLIFF WATCH THE MERMAID RETURN TO THE DEPTHS OF THE SEA. IT IS THEN THAT PRINCE VALIANT REMEMBERS MERLIN SAYING: *"THE SUPERNATURAL ALWAYS HAS A RATIONAL EXPLANATION."* HE DETERMINES TO SEEK THE ANSWER TO THIS MYSTERY.

AS HE CLIMBS DOWN THE CLIFF HIS COMPANIONS WARN HIM OF THE DANGER OF MEDDLING IN THE AFFAIRS OF THE MAGICAL BEINGS.

CLIMBING AMONG THE ROCKS AT THE WATER'S EDGE NEAR THE SPOT WHERE THE MAID DISAPPEARED, HE DISCOVERS AN ENTRANCE TO A GROTTO. HERE HE SITS DOWN TO WAIT, FOR THERE IS A DEEP SUSPICION IN HIS MIND.

IN A FEW MINUTES HIS SUSPICIONS ARE CONFIRMED. ALETA POPS OUT, NOW CLOTHED IN BATHING ATTIRE THAT EVEN THE MOST PRUDISH WOULD APPROVE.
"SO, MY WIFE HAS NOW BECOME A LEGEND," HE SCOLDS, *"A MYTHICAL DENIZEN OF THE DEEP. THANK HEAVEN FOR YOUR LONG HAIR!"*

"I SWIM AS I PLEASE," SHE SNAPS. *"I HAVE THE WHOLE WIDE SEA TO MYSELF."*
"BUT NOT THE LAND," VAL ANSWERS. *"LOOK TO THE TOP OF THE CLIFF."* ALETA TAKES A PEEK AND BLUSHES A BRIGHT PINK.
"OH, DEAR ME," SHE EXCLAIMS WEAKLY.

VAL CLIMBS UP TO HIS COMPANIONS. *"IT WAS NOT A SIREN,"* HE ANNOUNCES. *"POSSIBLY A MERMAID WHO LIVES IN A SEA CAVE UNDER THE CLIFF. PERFECTLY HARMLESS. SHALL WE GO?"*

1554 © King Features Syndicate, Inc., 1966. World rights reserved. 11-20

VAL THOROUGHLY ENJOYS THE NEXT FEW DAYS. HIS WIFE IS NOT AS ROYALLY AUTOCRATIC AS USUAL, BUT CHASTENED AND ALMOST DEMURE. HE MAKES THE MOST OF IT, FOR IT WILL NOT LAST LONG.

NEXT WEEK— **Back to Romance**

HAL FOSTER

Our Story: A COLD MISTY RAIN SPOILS THEIR SEASHORE HOLIDAY AND PRINCE VALIANT SUGGESTS THEY RIDE BACK TO CAMELOT. AT THE MENTION OF CAMELOT THE TWINS SUDDENLY REMEMBER THEIR UNDYING LOVE FOR THEIR CHOSEN KNIGHT CHAMPION, SIR HOWARD.

ROMANCE ALWAYS COMES TO PRINCESSES, (SO THE TROUBADORS SING) BUT KAREN AND VALETA DO NOT INTEND TO LEAVE IT TO CHANCE. THEY WANT ROMANCE NOW. HOWARD IS THEIR TARGET WHETHER HE LIKES IT OR NOT.

IN THEIR ABSENCE 'THAT WOMAN' HAS HOWARD SO BEMUSED THAT HE HAS FORGOTTEN TO SLAY EVEN A SMALL DRAGON IN HONOR OF HIS TWO ROMANTIC LADIES.

THE TWINS FIND THEIR FAITHLESS CHAMPION IN THE MIDST OF HIS GUILT AND DEMAND A SHOWDOWN. "WILL YOU MARRY US OR FACE OUR FATHER IN A DUEL FOR OUR HONOR?" ASKS KAREN WRATHFULLY. 'THAT WOMAN' ANSWERS — "IT IS UNLAWFUL TO HAVE TWO WIVES, EVEN TWINS. YOU MUST CHOOSE BETWEEN YOU."

"THEN HE CAN MARRY ME AND VALETA CAN BE MY LADY-IN-WAITING." TO KAREN THE MATTER IS SETTLED.
"WHAT! BE YOUR LADY-IN-WAITING!" SCREAMS VALETA. "YOU DON'T EVEN WASH BEHIND YOUR EARS AND YOU HAVE FLEAS!" AND THE FIGHT IS ON ...... AND OVER AS QUICKLY.

THEY SEEK OUT THE COURT MUSICIAN WHO HAS SUNG SO BEAUTIFULLY OF ROMANCE. HE UNDERSTANDS; NOW HE SINGS OF BLIGHTED LOVE, THE SMILE THAT HIDES A BROKEN HEART, THE GAY LAUGH THAT COVERS TRAGEDY.

1555   © King Features Syndicate, Inc., 1966. World rights reserved.   11-27

ALL DAY THEY ENJOY THEIR SWEET SORROW. THERE IS TALK OF ENDING THEIR PAIN WITH POISON OR ENTERING A CONVENT, BUT A LOST LOVE CANNOT COMPETE WITH AN EMPTY STOMACH. BY DINNER TIME THEY ARE BACK TO NORMAL.

HOWEVER, SOME TRAGEDIES ARE REAL, AND SORROW MARKS THE FACE OF AN AGED WARRIOR WHO RIDES INTO CAMELOT WITH A STORY TO TELL.

NEXT WEEK— *The Missing Heir*

Prince Valiant
IN THE DAYS OF KING ARTHUR
BY HAROLD R FOSTER

Our Story: AN AGED WARRIOR ENTERS CAMELOT AND SEEKS AUDIENCE WITH THE KING. SOON THEREAFTER PRINCE VALIANT IS SUMMONED AND ARTHUR SAYS: "BALA BURWULF ASKS OUR HELP, BUT LET HIM REPEAT HIS STORY TO YOU."
"I AM CHANCELLOR TO KING BEDWIN OF DINMORE, LONG A FAITHFUL FOLLOWER OF KING ARTHUR," BEGINS THE OLD MAN. "KING BEDWIN IS FULL OF YEARS AND HIS DAYS ARE NUMBERED. HIS SON, PRINCE HARWICK, HAS DISAPPEARED AND THIS POSES A PROBLEM."

"SHOULD THE KING DIE AND THE THRONE BE UNOCCUPIED HIS TWO BROTHERS WILL CONTEND FOR IT AND A RUINOUS WAR WILL FOLLOW. PRINCE HARWICK MUST BE FOUND!"

"I CAN CALL UPON LAUNCELOT TO LEAD AN ARMY OR SIR GAWAIN FOR SINGLE COMBAT," ARTHUR SAYS, "BUT THIS CALLS FOR SUBTLETY, FOR HARWICK MUST BE THERE TO FILL THE THRONE WHEN THE KING DIES. SO I HAVE CHOSEN YOU, VAL."

WHEN HE GOES TO BID FAREWELL TO ALETA SHE IS SHARING AN AFTERNOON NAP WITH GALAN. FOR A LONG WHILE HE FEASTS HIS EYES ON HER SERENE FACE, FOR HE MUST STORE UP MEMORIES TO LAST UNTIL HIS RETURN.

THEN HE TIPTOES OUT SO AS NOT TO DISTURB HER DREAMS.

"IS THERE ANYTHING YOU CAN TELL ME ABOUT PRINCE HARWICK THAT MIGHT AID ME IN MY SEARCH FOR HIM?" ASKS VAL. "YES, HE HATED COURT LIFE," ANSWERS THE OLD CHANCELLOR, "AND SPENT HIS TIME FISHING FOR SALMON AND TROUT OR HAWKING."

1558

"HIS FATHER, THE KING, WAS STRICT AND VERY SEVERE. THE TWO QUARRELED OFTEN, THEN THE BOY WOULD TAKE HIS NEW-FANGLED FISHING TOOLS AND SPEND THE DAY ON THE RIVER."
NEXT WEEK— The Salmon Fisherman

Prince Valiant

IN THE DAYS OF KING ARTHUR
BY HAROLD R. FOSTER

Our Story: THE OLD CHANCELLOR LEADS PRINCE VALIANT INTO THE TINY KINGDOM OF DINMORE, AND WHEN THE KING'S CASTLE COMES IN SIGHT VAL HALTS. "HERE I MUST LEAVE YOU," HE SAYS. "IF I AM TO SEARCH FOR PRINCE HARWICK IT IS BEST I REMAIN UNKNOWN."

AS THE MISSING HEIR SPENDS ALL HIS TIME HAWKING AND FISHING FOR SALMON, VAL FOLLOWS THE RIVERS, ASKING ALL HE MEETS ABOUT THE FISHING. "THIS RIVER IS FAMOUS FOR ITS SALMON, "A WOODCUTTER TELLS HIM, "EVEN NOW A FISHERMAN IS USING STRANGE METHODS TO CATCH THEM."

COULD THIS BE THE RUNAWAY PRINCE? FROM A DISTANCE VAL OBSERVES A PLUMP YOUNG MAN CASTING WITH ROD AND LINE. UP TO NOW SALMON HAVE BEEN TAKEN ONLY BY SPEAR OR NET, BUT THIS FELLOW HOOKS AND LANDS ONE!

VAL, AN ARDENT FISHERMAN HIMSELF, MUST LEARN THE SECRET OF THIS SPORTING WAY OF TAKING SALMON. HE FOLLOWS THE YOUTH AND HIS COMPANION AND TAKES LODGINGS AT THE SAME INN. THE INNKEEPER TELLS HIM THE YOUTH IS A TROUBADOR NAMED OWEN.

DURING HIS WANDERINGS VAL HAS OFTEN PROVIDED A TROUT DINNER BY TRAILING A HOOK DECORATED WITH SMALL FEATHERS IN A TROUT STREAM. NOW HE BEGINS TO TIE A FEW FLIES, KNOWING THIS WILL BE IRRESISTIBLE TO ANOTHER FISHERMAN.

"PARDON MY INTRUSION. MY NAME IS OWEN AND I SEE YOU KNOW MY SECRET OF TAKING SALMON." "NOT SO," ANSWERS VAL. "THESE FEATHERED HOOKS REPRESENT INSECTS AND ARE USED FOR TROUT. SALMON WILL NOT TAKE THEM."

"OH, BUT THEY WILL!" CRIES OWEN. "IN THE MORNING I WILL SHOW YOU, FOR YOU ARE A FISHERMAN AND THEREFORE A BROTHER."

CAN THIS CHUBBY LITTLE MAN BE THE CROWN PRINCE? VAL MUST BE SURE BEFORE HE SENDS A MESSAGE TO THE CHANCELLOR.

NEXT WEEK— The Promise

1557

12-11

Our Story: TRUE TO HIS PROMISE, OWEN, THE TROUBADOR, TAKES PRINCE VALIANT TO THE STREAM TO TEACH HIM HOW TO TAKE SALMON ON A FEATHERED HOOK. THE INNKEEPER'S DAUGHTER INSISTS ON CARRYING THE RODS AND LUNCH HAMPER.

EACH HAS HIS OWN PRIVATE THOUGHTS: *"CAN THIS HAPPY YOUTH BE THE MISSING HEIR TO THE THRONE OF DINMORE?"* DESPITE HIS PLAIN GARMENTS AND SIMPLE WAYS HIS BEARING IS THAT OF A GENTLEMAN BORN.

OWEN MEASURES HIS COMPANION: *"NO ORDINARY WARRIOR IS HE. GOLD ARM BANDS AND NECKLACE, JEWELS IN THE HILT OF HIS GREAT SWORD, AND HIS CREST, THE CRIMSON STALLION. WHERE HAS HE HEARD OF THAT CREST? HE IS OBVIOUSLY A FELLOW OF THE ROUND TABLE."*

"STRIP ENOUGH LINE TO REACH ACROSS THE RIVER," INSTRUCTS OWEN. *"THE ROD IS AS A BOW, THE HEAVY LINE THE ARROW. THROW AND THE HEAVY LINE WILL TAKE OUT THE SLACK."* VAL IS SO INTERESTED IN LEARNING TO CAST THAT HE ALMOST FORGETS THERE ARE SALMON THERE.

HE TRIES TO HALT THE LEAPING RUN BY HOLDING THE LINE AND IS REWARDED WITH SEVERELY BURNED FINGERS. TWO MORE SALMON ARE LOST ERE HE LEARNS TO PLAY THEM.

VAL IS MOST ENTHUSIASTIC AND WANTS TO KNOW WHAT WOOD IS BEST FOR A ROD, HOW TO BRAID A LINE AND WHIP ON THE GUIDES, ETC.

1558   © King Features Syndicate, Inc., 1966. World rights reserved.   12-18

AFTER DINNER THEY ARE DISCUSSING TACKLE WHEN OWEN SAYS: *"I WILL TELL YOU SOMETHING IF YOU GIVE YOUR KNIGHTLY WORD TO KEEP IT A SECRET."*
"OF COURSE," VAL PROMISES.
WITH A SLY GRIN OWEN ANSWERS: *"I AM PRINCE HARWICK, HEIR TO THE DINMORE THRONE."*
"AND," VAL SAYS, *"I WAS SENT TO FIND YOU AND BRING YOU BACK. BUT YOU HAVE MY OATH; YOUR SECRET IS SAFE."*

NEXT WEEK— *Harwick's Story*

1558

Prince Valiant
IN THE DAYS OF KING ARTHUR
BY HAROLD R. FOSTER

Our Story: PRINCE VALIANT HAS BEEN TRICKED! HE IS SENT ON A MISSION TO FIND THE RUNAWAY PRINCE HARWICK, AND THAT CLEVER YOUNG MAN SECURES VAL'S PROMISE TO KEEP HIS WHEREABOUTS A SECRET. WHICH COURSE SHOULD HE FOLLOW: HIS DUTY TO THE KING OR HIS OWN GIVEN WORD?

"YOU MAY WONDER WHY I GIVE UP RICHES AND POWER FOR THE LIFE OF SIMPLE LEISURE. WELL, AFTER MY MOTHER DIED, MY SIRE TOOK OVER MY SCHOOLING. DAY AFTER DAY I SAT IN A STUFFY ROOM AND STUDIED GOVERNMENT, LAW AND HISTORY...."

"AND UNDER HIS STERN EYE I WAS FORCED TO PRACTICE AT ARMS UNTIL TOO WEARY FOR PLAY WITH OTHER BOYS."

"WHEN I ATTAINED MANHOOD THE VERY THOUGHT OF ASCENDING TO THE THRONE OF DINMORE WAS HATEFUL. I REBELLED AND SOUGHT PEACE AND PLEASURE IN FIELD AND STREAM. MY FATHER, THE KING, SCOLDED ME ENDLESSLY."

"ONCE I WANDERED FAR FROM HOME AND FOUND THIS PLEASANT LITTLE INN AND MET RUTH, THE INNKEEPER'S DAUGHTER. I FELL IN LOVE WITH HER FRESH YOUNG BEAUTY. THE PERFUMED LADIES AT COURT COULD NOT MATCH HER SIMPLE, FRANK HONESTY. I INTEND TO MARRY HER AND SETTLE IN THIS LITTLE HEAVEN."

IN HIS GREAT BED KING BEDWIN OF DINMORE LIES PALE AND WEAK AS IF RESTING FOR HIS LONG JOURNEY INTO THE UNKNOWN. SHOULD THE THRONE BE VACANT WHEN HE DIES, TWO CLAIMANTS WILL CONTEND AND CIVIL WAR WILL DRENCH THE SMALL KINGDOM IN BLOOD.

1559

12-25

THE OLD CHANCELLOR HAS SPENT HIS LIFE IN FAITHFUL SERVICE TO HIS KING AND COUNTRY, BUT NOW, UNLESS THE CROWN PRINCE IS FOUND AND BROUGHT BACK, ALL HIS WORK WILL GO DOWN IN RUIN.

NEXT WEEK— Dark Clouds Gather

1559

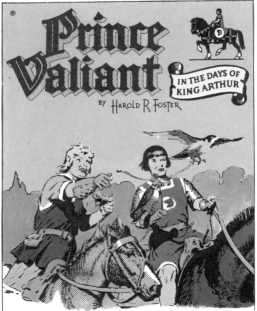

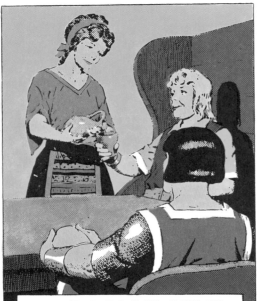

Prince Valiant
IN THE DAYS OF KING ARTHUR
BY HAROLD R FOSTER

Our Story: PRINCE VALIANT SPENDS PLEASANT DAYS WITH PRINCE HARWICK FISHING AND HAWKING BUT ALWAYS SEARCHING FOR SOME WAY TO KEEP HIS OATH OF SILENCE AND YET DISCHARGE HIS DUTY TO ARTHUR.

AS VAL WATCHES THE YOUNG LOVERS THE THRONE OF DINMORE SEEMS A TRIVIAL THING COMPARED TO RUTH'S FAIR FACE AND THE EAGER EYES THAT EXPRESS SO MUCH LOVE FOR HER GAY TROUBADOR. WHAT WOULD HAPPEN SHOULD SHE FIND OUT HE IS A PRINCE?

SOON THE TIME COMES WHEN THE OLD CHANCELLOR SENDS EVERYONE FROM THE KING'S CHAMBER AND IN SILENCE PULLS THE SHEET OVER HIS BEST FRIEND'S TIRED FACE. THE THRONE IS EMPTY.

AFTER A LONG WHILE THE CHANCELLOR RISES AND WIPES HIS EYES. THEN HE SENDS FOR THOSE WHO HAD ATTENDED THE KING IN HIS LAST DAYS. *"NO ONE MUST KNOW THE KING IS DEAD,"* HE COMMANDS, *"GO IN AND OUT OF THIS CHAMBER AS USUAL. THE FATE OF THE KINGDOM HANGS ON YOUR SECRECY."*

THE KING'S TWO YOUNGER BROTHERS WAIT ANXIOUSLY FOR NEWS OF THE KING'S DEATH. BOTH KNOW THE HEIR IS MISSING, BOTH LUST FOR THE POWER OF KINGSHIP. HE WHO SITS ON THE THRONE CAN FIND MEANS TO ELIMINATE ALL OTHER CLAIMANTS. EACH IS SECRETLY MASSING AN ARMY.

OUT OF THE ROYAL CASTLE SPEED MANY HORSEMEN WITH ORDERS TO FIND THE PRINCE BEFORE IT IS TOO LATE.

1560   © King Features Syndicate, Inc., 1966. World rights reserved.

ON A RAINY EVENING A WEARY TRAVELER ENTERS THE INN AND CALLS FOR REFRESHMENT. THEN HE GLANCES AROUND AND LEAVES HURRIEDLY.....

....AND RETURNS BY THE ROAD ON WHICH HE CAME.

NEXT WEEK- **The Wine Flask**

Prince Valiant

IN THE DAYS OF KING ARTHUR

BY HAROLD R. FOSTER

Our Story: PRINCE VALIANT IS IN A DILEMMA. HIS MISSION IS TO FIND THE MISSING PRINCE HARWICK, BUT THE CLEVER PRINCE HAS TRICKED HIM INTO PROMISING NOT TO TELL HIS WHERE-ABOUTS. OH, WELL, HE WILL FIND OUT WHICH WAY HIS DUTY LIES, AND IN THE MEANTIME THE DAYS PASS PLEASANTLY.

THE INN DOOR OPENS AND THERE STANDS THE OLD CHANCELLOR. *"THE KING IS DEAD,"* HE ANNOUNCES. *"LONG LIVE THE KING!"*

"WHAT CARE I OF KINGS AND THRONES?" LAUGHS THE PLUMP YOUTH. *"I AM OWEN, A HUMBLE TROUBADOR SEEKING ONLY PEACE AND CONTENTMENT. HERE I FIND IT, HERE I STAY."*

HE IS REMINDED OF HIS ROYAL BLOOD, HIS DUTY TO HIS KINGDOM, THE WELFARE OF HIS PEOPLE, THE THREAT OF RUINOUS WAR. BUT OWEN IS UNMOVED: *"MY ROYAL THRONE, HAH!"* HE SCOFFS. *"CHAINED TO IT BY RESPONSIBILITIES, MY DAYS SPENT IN LISTENING TO WHINING COMPLAINTS. NO! MY THRONE IS THE HEART OF RUTH, HER LOVE MY ONLY KINGDOM."*

"RUTH, MY CHILD, WE HAVE GRAVE MATTERS TO DISCUSS, SO DO TAKE YOUR SUPPER TO YOUR ROOM. AND HERE IS A FLASK OF FINE WINE, WORTHY OF A KING'S TABLE."

RUTH IS PUZZLED WITH ALL THIS TALK OF KINGS AND THRONES. WHAT HAS HER OWEN TO DO WITH SUCH MATTERS?

THEIR MEAL IS INTERRUPTED BY A SCREAM; A MAID STUMBLES DOWN THE STAIRS. *"IT IS RUTH! SHE IS LYING SO STILL... SHE... SHE IS DEAD!"*

NEXT WEEK— **Long Live the King**

1561   © King Features Syndicate, Inc., 1967. World rights reserved   1-8

Prince Valiant
IN THE DAYS OF KING ARTHUR
BY Harold R Foster

Our Story: *"RUTH IS DEAD!"* SCREAMS THE SERVANT. THERE IS A STUNNED SILENCE. ONLY MINUTES AGO SHE WAS ROSY WITH HEALTH AND TRIPPED UPSTAIRS ON LIGHT FEET!
IN HER TIDY ROOM SHE LIES ON HER BED, HER FACE SERENE, NO SIGN OF WOUND OR PAIN. THE CHANCELLOR FILLS A GOBLET FROM THE WINE FLASK.

"LONG LIVE THE KING!" HE SAYS AND DRAINS THE GOBLET. *"YES, I KILLED HER. SHE WAS SO LOVELY THAT PRINCE HARWICK WOULD NEVER HAVE LEFT HER FOR THE THRONE."*

"YOU FIEND!" HISSES HARWICK, *"OH, MAY YOU BE DAMNED FOR THIS FOUL DEED!"*
"DOUBLY DAMNED," CORRECTS THE OLD CHANCELLOR, *"FOR THE WINE IS POISONED AND I HAVE TAKEN MY OWN LIFE ALSO. BUT YOU ARE NOW KING WHETHER YOU WISH IT OR NOT. FOOL YOU WERE TO THINK THAT THOSE OF ROYAL BLOOD COULD EXCHANGE THE LONELINESS AND RESPONSIBILITY OF THE THRONE FOR A LIFE OF CONTENTMENT AND EASE. DOUBLY DAMNED, YES, BUT THE THRONE IS FILLED AND OUR LITTLE KINGDOM SAVED FROM A BLOODY CIVIL WAR..... AND I AM CONTENT."*

NEXT WEEK—*The Passing Storm*

HAL FOSTER

1562

1-15

Prince Valiant
IN THE DAYS OF KING ARTHUR
BY HAROLD R. FOSTER

Our Story: TRAGEDY BRINGS THE UNWANTED THRONE OF DINMORE TO PRINCE HARWICK. HIS FEW BRIEF DAYS OF FREEDOM AND ROMANCE END IN A CUP OF POISONED WINE.

AFTER HOURS OF GRIM SILENCE HARWICK TURNS FURIOUSLY ON PRINCE VALIANT; *"TRAITOR,"* HE SNARLS, *"IT WAS YOU WHO BETRAYED ME TO THE CHANCELLOR. WHO ELSE KNEW MY WHEREABOUTS? YOU BROKE YOUR GIVEN WORD!"*

EVEN AS THEIR SWORDS COME WHISPERING FROM THEIR SCABBARDS A CAPTAIN OF THE GUARDS SPURS BETWEEN THEM. *"NAY, MY LIEGE,"* HE CRIES, *"YOU WERE NOT BETRAYED. WE SEARCHED FOR YOU BUT FAILED BECAUSE OF YOUR DISGUISE."*

"THE CHANCELLOR WAS CONFIDENT SIR VALIANT WOULD FIND YOU AND BID US FOLLOW HIS TRAIL. IT WAS EASY, AS EVERYONE NOTED THE PASSING OF AN ARMED KNIGHT."
"I APOLOGIZE, VAL. A FOOL WAS I TO THINK YOU WOULD BREAK YOUR PROMISE. I AM SORRY."

THE PASSING OF THE OLD KING AND THE FINDING OF PRINCE HARWICK HAVE BEEN KEPT SECRET, BUT THE TWO UNCLES THINK IT HIGH TIME FOR EACH TO MAKE HIS OWN BID FOR THE THRONE. IF THE KING IS STILL ALIVE THEY CAN HASTEN HIS END.

HARWICK ENTERS THE CASTLE AND IS TOLD BY THE SCOUTS OF HIS UNCLES' PLOTS. MORE SCOUTS AND SWIFT MESSENGERS ARE SENT OUT TO KEEP WATCH ON THE MOVEMENTS OF THE PLOTTERS. THEN, IN A VERY BRIEF CEREMONY, HARWICK IS CROWNED KING.

THE NEW KING APPEARS DRESSED IN HIS FATHER'S WAR HARNESS. *"I GO TO CONFRONT MY UNCLES, AND I WOULD LIKE TO HAVE YOU AT MY SIDE, SIR VALIANT. YOU MAY, WITH HONOR, REFUSE SUCH A DANGEROUS EFFORT, FOR YOUR MISSION HAS BEEN COMPLETED."*
VAL GRINS; THE ODDS ARE ATTRACTIVE, TWO AGAINST TWO ARMIES!
"SHALL WE RIDE, SIRE?" HE ASKS.
NEXT WEEK— *"I am your leader!"*

Prince Valiant

IN THE DAYS OF KING ARTHUR

BY HAROLD R FOSTER

Our Story: THE NEWLY CROWNED KING HARWICK RIDES OUT FROM THE SAFETY OF HIS CASTLE TO ENCOUNTER THE ARMIES OF TWO CLAIMANTS TO HIS THRONE. PRINCE VALIANT GOES ALONG FOR THE EXERCISE.

A GREAT CHANGE HAS COME OVER THE PLUMP KING. THE LONG HOURS OF STUDY AND THE HARSH TRAINING THAT HAD MADE HIS POSITION SO HATEFUL AND CAUSED HIM TO RUN AWAY NOW SHOW UP IN HIS CONFIDENT BEARING.

SCOUTS KEEP THEM INFORMED OF THE MOVEMENTS OF THE TWO ARMIES. *"MY DEAR UNCLE CURWIN IS THE CLOSEST. WE WILL VISIT HIM FIRST. ALTHOUGH A MAN OF GREAT FORCE, HE IS A BIT STUPID,"* SNEERS THE YOUNG KING.

DUKE CURWIN WATCHES THE TWO HORSEMEN APPROACH IN GROWING FEAR, FOR ONE OF THEM IS PRINCE HARWICK WEARING THE KING'S ARMOR. THAT CAN MEAN ONLY ONE THING, AND BEFORE THE DUKE CAN DEVISE ANY TREACHERY THE NEW KING CRIES: *"I AM YOUR KING, YOUR ROYAL LEADER! YOU WILL OBEY MY ORDERS!"*

"LINE UP YOUR MEN, I WISH TO CHOOSE A BODYGUARD," IS HIS FIRST COMMAND, AND THEREAFTER HE PICKS OUT THE BEST OF HIS UNCLE'S WARRIORS. IN HELPLESS RAGE CURWIN WATCHES HIS STRENGTH FADE AWAY. FOR IT IS AN HONOR TO SERVE AS A ROYAL BODYGUARD AND THESE MEN ARE LOST TO HIM FOREVER.

"NOW WE GO TO MEET YOUR SLY BROTHER AND DISSUADE HIM FROM DOING SOMETHING HE MIGHT REGRET." THE FAT LITTLE PRINCE, WHO HAD ONLY WANTED TO PLAY, HAS MADE A FRIGHTENING CHANGE. THE DUKE OBEYS.

1564 © King Features Syndicate, Inc., 1967. World rights reserved. 1-29

WORD HAS REACHED THE EARL OF GROSMONT THAT HIS BROTHER IS MARCHING ON THE CAPITAL WITH HIS ARMY. HE WOULD RATHER DEPEND ON TRICKERY AND DECEIT, BUT THIS CALLS FOR A SURPRISE ATTACK IN FORCE.

EVEN AS HE IS PLANNING A NIGHT ASSAULT ON A SLEEPING ARMY, THAT ARMY APPEARS. FEAR GRIPS HIM AS HE RECOGNIZES THE LEADER, WEARING THE ROYAL ARMOR!

NEXT WEEK- *A King earns a Throne*

Prince Valiant
IN THE DAYS OF KING ARTHUR
BY HAROLD R. FOSTER

Our Story: THE EARL OF GROSMONT HAS SPENT A LIFETIME PLOTTING TO GAIN THE THRONE OF DINMORE. NOW HIS DREAMS FADE AS HIS BROTHER'S ARMY APPROACHES LED BY THE NEW KING. AT A WORD FROM PRINCE VALIANT THE BODYGUARD FORMS A WEDGE FORCING A WIDE PASSAGE.

"LONG LIVE THE KING!" EXCLAIMS THE EARL. "I WAS ON MY WAY TO PROTECT YOUR THRONE UNTIL YOUR RETURN, MY LIEGE," AND HE BOWS LOW TO HIDE THE MALICE IN HIS EYES.

"THEN YOU MAY STILL VISIT OUR CASTLE," ANSWERS HARWICK, "BUT YOU CAN SEND YOUR ARMY BACK, AS I ALREADY HAVE ONE." THE RIDE TO THE ROYAL CASTLE IS NOT A PLEASANT ONE FOR THE TWO BROTHERS. THEY FEEL LIKE PRISONERS AND SUSPECT THEY ARE.

TO ADD TO THEIR FEAR IS THE ATTENTION OF THAT KNIGHT, SIR VALIANT. HE IS FOREVER CARESSING THE HILT OF HIS GREAT SWORD AND LOOKS AS IF HE WOULD ENJOY SOME LIGHT EXERCISE.

THE BROTHERS WILLINGLY TAKE THE OATH OF FEALTY TO THE NEPHEW THEY HAVE DESPISED AS A FAT LITTLE PLAYBOY. HOW MISTAKEN THEY HAVE BEEN, AND IT WOULD BE WELL TO REMEMBER HOW CLOSE THEY CAME TO THE HEADSMAN'S BLOCK.

1565

2-5

"AND I, WHO SAID I WOULD NEVER BE KING, FIND MYSELF NURSEMAID TO A KINGDOM, A SERVANT TO MY PEOPLE. THE OLD CHANCELLOR WAS RIGHT: WE OF ROYAL BLOOD CANNOT AVOID OUR DESTINY."

NEXT WEEK—The Unjust Justice

Prince Valiant

IN THE DAYS OF KING ARTHUR

BY Harold R. Foster

Our Story: THE MURDER OF HIS SWEETHEART AND THE DEATH OF THE CHANCELLOR HAVE BROUGHT HARWICK TO THE UNWANTED THRONE. A TRAGIC FIGURE WITH THE POWER OF LIFE AND DEATH OVER HIS SUBJECTS, HE SITS IN HIS HALL OF JUSTICE.

HE ADMINISTERS JUSTICE ACCORDING TO ANCIENT LAW: A THIEF MUST LOSE A HAND, A RUNAWAY SERF REDUCED TO SLAVERY, DEATH TO A BONDSMAN WHO RAISED HIS HAND IN ANGER AGAINST AN OVERSEER. ONLY WHEN SENTENCE HAS BEEN PASSED DOES THE KING ASK: "DOES ANYONE SPEAK IN BEHALF OF THE ACCUSED?"

PRINCE VALIANT STEPS FORWARD. "I WILL BE THEIR ADVOCATE. STAY THE EXECUTIONER AND LET ME SPEAK WITH THEM FOR AN HOUR. JUSTICE HAS BEEN DONE, NO DOUBT, BUT A JUSTICE WITHOUT MERCY OR UNDERSTANDING."

AT HOUR'S END VAL RETURNS WITH THE PRISONERS. "THE ACCUSED THIEF WAS ONCE A SOLDIER IN THE KING'S ARMY. HIS BATTLE WOUNDS MADE HIM UNFIT FOR SERVICE. A CRIPPLE, HE COULD NOT FIND EMPLOYMENT. YES, HE STOLE, STOLE FOOD TO SAVE HIS FAMILY FROM STARVATION. WHAT WILL BE HIS REWARD FOR A LIFETIME OF SERVICE TO HIS KING AND COUNTRY?"

"THIS WOMAN LEFT HER VILLAGE WITHOUT PERMISSION TO ATTEND HER DAUGHTER IN CHILDBIRTH. IS MOTHER LOVE A CRIME DESERVING SLAVERY?"

1566   2-12

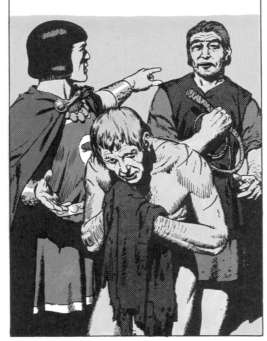

"THANK YOU, VAL," SAYS KING HARWICK QUIETLY. "I HAVE BEEN TOO OCCUPIED WITH MY OWN DESPAIR. OH, HOW I WISH THE OLD CHANCELLOR WERE HERE TO ADVISE. TO BE A KING IS MY DESTINY, BUT I WISH TO BE A GOOD ONE!"

NEXT WEEK - Enter Sir Reynolde.

Prince Valiant

IN THE DAYS OF KING ARTHUR

BY HAROLD R. FOSTER

Our Story: THE YEARS OF RELENTLESS TRAINING FOR KINGSHIP HAD CAUSED YOUNG PRINCE HARWICK TO HATE THE VERY THOUGHT OF TAKING THE THRONE. BUT NOW THAT HE IS KING NO ONE MAY GIVE HIM ORDERS, ALL AUTHORITY IS IN HIS HANDS, AND HE ACCEPTS THE RESPONSIBILITY.

"I AM GLAD YOU TOLD ME OF KING ARTHUR'S METHOD OF ADMINISTERING JUSTICE. I SHALL CHANGE OUR ANCIENT LAWS SO THE ACCUSED MAY HAVE A CHANCE TO SPEAK IN THEIR OWN DEFENSE. AND WHAT ARE YOU WORKING ON, VAL?"

"FISHING TACKLE SUCH AS YOU INVENTED, BUT WITH MANY IMPROVEMENTS," ANSWERS VAL. *"MY WORK HERE IS FINISHED, BUT ON MY RETURN TO CAMELOT I WILL DINE ROYALLY ON TROUT AND SALMON."*

VAL BIDS FAREWELL TO YOUNG KING HARWICK AND IS ABOUT TO MOUNT WHEN A YOUNG NOBLE APPROACHES AND ASKS IF HE MAY JOIN HIM ON HIS JOURNEY TO CAMELOT AND THERE SEEK HIS FORTUNE.

HIS NAME IS SIR REYNOLDE, AND HE PROVES TO BE A MERRY YOUTH AND A GOOD COMPANION. A SPARKLING RIVER TEMPTS VAL TO TRY OUT HIS NEW FISHING TACKLE, SO THEY HALT WHILE REYNOLDE SETS UP CAMP.

VAL SOON LEARNS THAT FLY FISHING HAS MANY PROBLEMS. ALTHOUGH HE MAY HAVE BEEN THE FIRST TO ENCOUNTER THEM, THEY HAVE REMAINED UNSOLVED, EVEN TODAY.

1567   © King Features Syndicate, Inc., 1967. World rights reserved.   2-19

HE CONTINUES TO MAKE HISTORY, AND SOME OF THE EXPRESSIONS HE USES ARE STILL COMMON AMONG FISHERMEN.

UNABLE TO GAIN HIS FEET BECAUSE OF THE FORCE OF THE WATER, HE BUMPS UNHAPPILY DOWNSTREAM. NEVER HAS HIS ENTHUSIASM FOR FISHING REACHED SUCH A LOW EBB.

NEXT WEEK—*Actors All*

HAL FOSTER

Prince Valiant

IN THE DAYS OF KING ARTHUR

BY Harold R Foster

Our Story: A WATER-LOGGED PRINCE VALIANT ENDS HIS SWIFT DOWNSTREAM VOYAGE IN A QUIET POOL. THEN THE QUIET IS BROKEN BY MERRY VOICES: "SAIL HO! A STRANGE CRAFT APPROACHES!" AND "'TIS AN AMOROUS YOUTH SEEKING A WATER NYMPH!" ALSO "A MARINER HOME FROM THE SEA, WELCOME ASHORE!"

THEY TREAT HIS NARROW ESCAPE FROM DROWNING AS IF HE HAD PURPOSELY FALLEN INTO THE RAPIDS FOR THEIR AMUSEMENT. THEY TAKE HIM TO THEIR CAMP TO DRY OUT.

VAL FINDS HIMSELF WITH A TROUPE OF ACTORS SEEKING FAME AND FORTUNE ACROSS THE WHOLE WIDE WORLD. NOW THEY ARE BOUND FOR CALDERGARDE TO ENTERTAIN AT A WEDDING FEAST AND INVITE HIM TO JOIN THEM. HE AGREES, "I WILL GO FETCH MY BELONGINGS."

THERE HE INSTRUCTS SIR REYNOLDE, HIS TRAVELING COMPANION: "MEET ME AT CALDERGARDE, A DAY'S RIDE FROM HERE. I WILL TAKE THE BAGGAGE HORSE AND A FEW SIMPLE BELONGINGS AND TRAVEL WITH A TROUPE OF ENTERTAINERS. IT SHOULD BE FUN."

AND FUN IT IS. THEY SING ALONG THE WAY, MAKE JOKES, STEAL CHICKENS AND GEESE, AND PAY FOR THEIR MEAD AND ALE WITH A NEIGHBOR'S FOWL.

AT CALDERGARDE VAL GETS A SURPRISE. REYNOLDE HAS SHAVED, TRIMMED HIS HAIR AND IS WEARING VAL'S CLOTHES. "YOU ARE NOT USING YOUR IDENTITY, SO I HAVE BORROWED IT," HE EXPLAINS.

HAL FOSTER

"YOU, AS AN ACTOR, WILL EAT IN THE KITCHEN, SLEEP IN THE SHED; WHILE I, AS PRINCE VALIANT, WILL ENJOY BEING PAMPERED AS A FAMOUS KNIGHT! DO YOU AGREE?"

NEXT WEEK— Actors All

Prince Valiant
IN THE DAYS OF KING ARTHUR
BY Harold R Foster

Our Story: VAL, SITTING AT THE END OF THE LOWER TABLE AMONG THE JONGLEURS, WATCHES REYNOLDE, HIS TRAVELING COMPANION WHO, POSING AS PRINCE VALIANT, DINES IN STATE AT THE HIGH TABLE.

REYNOLDE IS WITTY AND QUITE AMUSING AND HIS MANNERS ARE BEYOND REPROACH, SO VAL IS ASSURED HIS IMITATOR WILL NOT SPOIL HIS IMAGE.

AS VAL OFTEN SINGS TO PASS THE LONELY HOURS OF HIS JOURNEYS HE IS IN GOOD VOICE. HE ENTERTAINS THE WEDDING GUESTS, THEREBY EARNING HIS KEEP AS A JONGLEUR.

AND NOW FOULK, ACTOR, AUTHOR, SINGER AND ALL-AROUND GENIUS, PUTS ON A PLAY HE HAS WRITTEN AND IN WHICH HE IS THE BRAVE HERO. HE RECEIVES A ROUSING OVATION, HELPED ALONG, NO DOUBT, BY THE ALE AND MEAD THE GUESTS HAVE CONSUMED.

STILL GIDDY FROM THE APPLAUSE FOULK DECLAIMS: "I AM INSPIRED TO WRITE ANOTHER PLAY. I TO BE LAUNCELOT AND YOU, SIR, WILL BE MY SQUIRE. IT WILL BE AN IMMORTAL ROMANCE, BUT WE WILL HAVE TO RECRUIT AN ACTRESS TO ROUND OUT THE CAST."

IN THE SHED WHERE THE JONGLEURS ARE QUARTERED A CANDLE BURNS ALL NIGHT AS FOULK WORKS ON HIS NEW PLAY. OCCASIONALLY HE MUTTERS: "GOOD, GOOD!" AND "EXCELLENT!" THEN, "OH, FOULK, HOW CLEVER YOU ARE, YOU ARE TOUCHED BY DIVINE GENIUS!"

"THE WEDDING PARTY IS OVER, THE GUESTS DEPARTING, AND WE JONGLEURS LEAVE FOR THE TOURNAMENT AT CASTLE GLENHAVEN. WE WILL CONTINUE OUR MASQUERADE FOR ANOTHER WEEK, REYNOLDE. DO YOU AGREE?"

NEXT WEEK—Lady Ann

1569

3-5

1569

Prince Valiant
IN THE DAYS OF KING ARTHUR
BY HAROLD R. FOSTER

Our Story: THE WEDDING FEAST AT CALDERGARDE IS OVER, THE GUESTS DEPARTING. FIRST TO LEAVE IS THE GROUP OF JONGLEURS AND IT IS SUSPECTED THAT MANY MISSING ARTICLES WENT WITH THEM. VAL IS ENJOYING HIS ROLE AS AN ENTERTAINER, AND REYNOLDE, MASQUERADING AS PRINCE VALIANT, LEARNS WHAT IT IS LIKE TO BEAR A FAMOUS NAME.

FOULK, LEADER OF THE ITINERANT PLAYERS, IS A FINE ACTOR AS ALL WITHIN SOUND OF HIS VOICE SOON LEARN.
"I HAVE A GENIUS FOR LIVING EACH CHARACTER I PLAY," HE DECLAIMS.

"WHEN I PLAY THE PART OF A KING, I AM A KING!"

"DO YOU WISH A BEGGAR? A BEGGAR AM I!"

"WHEN I PLAY A VILLAIN, I EVEN HATE MYSELF!"

"BUT AS A NOBLE HERO I DO NOT ACT... I AM!"

FOULK IS CARRIED AWAY BY HIS OWN BRAGGING. "LOOK, YOU, SIR VALIANT, WHEN WE REACH CASTLE GLENHAVEN I WILL ENTER AS YOUR NOBLE COMPANION, A FAR-WANDERING KNIGHT, A WARRIOR OF RENOWN. NO ONE WILL DOUBT ME. DO I HAVE YOUR PROMISE NOT TO BETRAY ME?"

GLENHAVEN IS ALL AFLUTTER WITH FLAGS AND BANNERS. TRUMPETS SOUND FROM THE COURTYARD WHERE PENNANTS FLY FROM THE PAVILIONS OF KNIGHTS GATHERING FOR THE TOURNAMENT. PRINCE VALIANT IS AMUSED AS HE LEADS A PACK-HORSE WHILE TWO IMITATION KNIGHTS RIDE IN STATE.

HAL FOSTER

A MAID WATCHES THE GUESTS ARRIVING AND THREE PAIRS OF DARK EYES GAZE AT HER, EACH WITH A DIFFERENT THOUGHT. SLIM AND GOLDEN WITH GREY EYES, VAL IS REMINDED OF ALETA WHEN FIRST HE SAW HER.
FOULK: "I SHALL TRY TO WIN HER AS A MEMBER OF MY TROOP, THEN FAME AND FORTUNE WILL BE MINE."
REYNOLDE'S MOUTH FALLS OPEN AND HIS HEART ROLLS OVER IN COMPLETE SURRENDER.
NEXT WEEK—The Rivals

1570   © King Features Syndicate, Inc., 1967. World rights reserved.   3-12

Prince Valiant
IN THE DAYS OF KING ARTHUR
BY HAROLD R FOSTER

Our Story: PRINCE VALIANT DINES IN THE KITCHEN WITH THE OTHER ENTERTAINERS, AND THE IRREPRESSIBLE JONGLEURS TURN THE MEAL INTO A NEAR RIOT. THE KITCHEN STAFF IS EITHER WEAK FROM LAUGHTER OR SCREAMING IN RAGE.

FOULK AND REYNOLDE ARE GREETED BY THEIR HOST: "WE HAVE HEARD MUCH OF YOUR DEEDS, SIR VALIANT, AND WE EXTEND OUR WELCOME TO YOUR FRIEND, SIR FOULK."

CONTESTS BETWEEN YEOMEN IN ARCHERY, WRESTLING AND RACING OPEN THE TOURNAMENT, AND THE LADY ANN IS AMUSED BY FOULK'S WITTY CONVERSATION, WHILE REYNOLDE SITS SHY AND TONGUE-TIED.

FOULK IS THE CENTER OF ATTENTION AT THE TABLE, FOR AS AN ACTOR HE HAS TRAVELED FAR AND WIDE AND HAS LEARNED MUCH. HE TELLS OF HIS ADVENTURES WITH LAUNCELOT, GAWAIN AND TRISTRAM. REYNOLDE IS SILENT, KNOWING ALL THESE TALES TO BE FALSE, BUT HE HAS GIVEN HIS PROMISE NOT TO EXPOSE FOULK.

IN ALL HER SIXTEEN YEARS THE LADY ANN HAS NEVER SEEN SO MANY GALLANT WARRIORS AS ARE GATHERED AT THIS TOURNAMENT. SHE IS FLATTERED THAT SO CHARMING A KNIGHT AS SIR FOULK SHOULD SEEK HER COMPANY.

REYNOLDE SUFFERS AS HE WATCHES THE GIRL HE LOVES BEING FASCINATED BY THE GLIB ACTOR. HOW CAN HE WARN HER WHEN HE TOO IS USING A NAME NOT HIS OWN?

1571

© King Features Syndicate, Inc. 1967. World rights reserved.   3-19

HAL FOSTER

A MINSTREL IS FREE TO WANDER WHERE HE WILL AND AMUSE THE GUESTS, SO VAL IS ABLE TO KEEP AN EYE ON HIS COMPANIONS AS ROMANCE BEGINS TO LEAD TOWARD TRAGEDY.

NEXT WEEK – *The Serpent and the Dove*

Prince Valiant
IN THE DAYS OF KING ARTHUR
BY Harold R Foster

Our Story: PRINCE VALIANT, IN THE GUISE OF A MINSTREL, SPIES SHAMELESSLY ON HIS TWO COMPANIONS AS THEY VIE FOR THE FAVOR OF LADY ANN. BUT THE COMEDY IS NEARING AN END, FOR REYNOLDE IS NOW WEARING VAL'S SWORD.

IT HAD BEEN FUN TO ASSUME THE CLOTHES AND NAME OF PRINCE VALIANT AND ENJOY THE FLATTERING ATTENTION THE NAME BROUGHT HIM. THEN HE FALLS IN LOVE WITH THE LADY ANN, AND THE MASQUERADE HAS BECOME A BURDEN.

FOULK, EVER THE ACTOR, PLAYS THE PART OF A WANDERING NOBLE WITH DELIGHT, BRAGS OF HIS EXPLOITS, AND MAKES LOVE TO LADY ANN. HE FEELS SAFE, FOR HE HAS PRINCE VALIANT'S PROMISE NOT TO EXPOSE HIM.

"WHEN CAN I END THIS FARCE?" WAILS REYNOLDE. "IT HAS GONE PAST A JOKE, AND IF I CONFESS TO THE FRAUD, THE LADY ANN WILL DESPISE ME, OUR HOST AND GUESTS WILL LAUGH AT MY PRESUMPTION!" VAL GRINS:— "PLAY YOUR PART UNTIL THE END AND SEE WHAT HAPPENS."

"ANN, ANN! COME AWAY FROM THIS DULL CASTLE LIFE. COME WITH ME AND ROAM THE WORLD, JOYOUS AND FREE UNDER SUNNY SKIES. REST IN LEAFY BOWERS WITH STARS OUR NIGHT LIGHT. I HAVE IT! WE WILL JOIN THE COMPANY OF TRAVELING PLAYERS AND AS ROMANTIC VAGABONDS ENTERTAIN IN PALACES AND THE COURTS OF KINGS!"

"HOW EXCITING IT WILL BE WHEN THE TWO FINEST ENTERTAINERS IN THE WORLD REVEAL THEMSELVES AS THE WEALTHY LADY ANN AND THE NOBLE SIR FOULK!"

FOULK MAKES HIS WAY UNSEEN TO THE STABLE WHERE THE ENTERTAINERS ARE QUARTERED. "SUCCESS!" HE CRIES. "I HAVE FOUND A FAIR MAID OF NOBLE BEARING TO JOIN OUR COMPANY. UNDER MY TUTORING SHE WILL BECOME THE FINE ACTRESS OUR PLAY NEEDS. OUR FORTUNES ARE MADE! BE READY TO LEAVE AT MIDNIGHT."

NEXT WEEK— Romance on the Rocks   3-26

HAL FOSTER

Our Story: VAL WATCHES FOULK SLINK INTO THE NIGHT. SO THIS GLIB MOUNTEBANK HAS CHARMED THE INNOCENT LADY ANN INTO ELOPING! HER ROMANTIC DREAMS WILL FADE ALONG THE MUDDY ROADS, IN THE RAIN AND COLD, SLEEPING IN LOFTS AND STABLES.

"REYNOLDE, FOULK IS ELOPING TONIGHT," GRINS VAL. "HE HAS FILLED ANN'S GIRLISH HEAD WITH ROMANTIC TALES OF WANDER-ING FAR AND FREE UNDER SUMMER SKIES. DO YOU HAVE A WEDDING GIFT FOR HIM?"
"YES!" ANSWERS REYNOLDE, GRIMLY BUCKLING ON HIS SWORD, "THIS!"

FOULK HAS ONE LAST WORD OF ADVICE: "BRING ALL YOUR RAIMENT AND JEWELS, EVEN SOME OF YOUR MOTHER'S IF YOU CAN GET THEM, FOR YOU MUST BE RESPLENDENT WHEN WE ENTER THE PALACES OF KINGS."

AS THEY CROSS THE MOONLIT COURTYARD ANN HAS A MOMENT OF MISGIVING WHEN THE GALLANT SWAIN ALLOWS HER TO CARRY HER BAGS OF CLOTHING WHILE HE FOLLOWS WITH HER JEWELRY.

HIS TROUPE OF JONGLEURS IS WAITING OUTSIDE THE CASTLE GATES. "LET US HASTEN ON OUR WAY," ORDERS FOULK, AND POINTING TO VAL, "YOU, TAKE YOUR LUGGAGE OFF THAT HORSE. THE LADY ANN MUST RIDE!"
"AS YOU WISH," ANSWERS VAL, AND MOONBEAMS FLASH FROM THE JEWELS ON THE 'SINGING SWORD.'

"PRINCE VALIANT!" EXCLAIMS FOULK. "NO!" REPLIES REYNOLDE. "THE MASQUE IS OVER. I AM ONLY REYNOLDE, SON OF SIR HUGO OF DINMORE. MY SWORD HAS NEVER BEEN TESTED IN BATTLE. I HOPE TO PUT IT TO THE TEST TONIGHT.

1573   © King Features Syndicate, Inc., 1967. World rights reserved   4-2

FOULK, ALWAYS THE ACTOR, CANNOT HELP DRAMATIZING THIS MOMENT. DRAWING HIS BLADE HE THUNDERS: "NO HARM WILL COME TO LADY ANN WHILE I STILL LIVE. I WILL DEFEND HER HONOR AGAINST ALL THE FIENDS OF HELL!"

"THEN YOU WILL NOT MIND CROSSING SWORDS WITH ME ALONE?" ASKS REYNOLDE FOULK HOLDS HIS HEROIC POSE, ONLY HIS EYES SHOW THE COLD FEAR HE FEELS.
NEXT WEEK—Is There No Honesty?

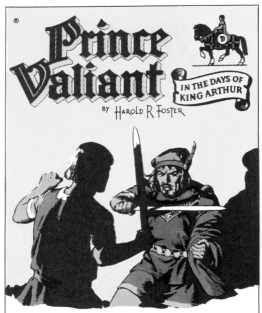

®

Prince Valiant
IN THE DAYS OF
KING ARTHUR
BY HAROLD R FOSTER

Our Story: FOULK, THE ACTOR, HAS PLAYED THE HERO SO OFTEN HE HAS COME TO BELIEVE HE REALLY IS ONE. NOW HE HAS MISGIVINGS AS THE GLEAMING BLADE IN REYNOLDE'S HAND REMINDS HIM THAT THIS IS REAL. HE BACKS AWAY.

WHEN HE CAN BACK NO FARTHER FEAR SEIZES HIM, HE SCREAMS, SLASHING WILDLY IN SHEER PANIC. REYNOLDE IS HARD PUT TO DEFEND HIMSELF AGAINST THIS FRENZY, BUT SUCCEEDS IN CAUSING A SMALL WOUND.

AT SIGHT OF HIS OWN BLOOD FOULK COLLAPSES. "SPARE ME, I AM WOUNDED, I CAN NO LONGER FIGHT. I YIELD, SPARE ME!" THE LADY ANN STANDS STIFF AND PROUD AND GIVES NOT A GLANCE AT THE CRAVEN SHE THOUGHT SHE LOVED.

"LADY ANN, MAY I ESCORT YOU? I HAVE SO MUCH TO TELL YOU." "NO! I HAVE SUFFERED MY FULL SHARE OF HUMILIATION; DECEIVED BY THE GLIB TONGUE OF A CRAVEN MOUNTEBANK WHO POSED AS A NOBLE, AND YOU...... A JACKDAW DRESSED IN AN EAGLE'S CLOTHES. EVEN PRINCE VALIANT WEARS THE RAGS OF A JONGLEUR. IS THERE NO HONESTY IN THIS WORLD?"

FOR ONCE THERE IS NEITHER SONG NOR JEST AS THE TROUPE OF WANDERING PLAYERS FOLLOWS AFTER THEIR RAPIDLY VANISHING LEADER.

"ANN, ANN! DO NOT JUDGE ME TOO HARSHLY. WE BUT PLAYED AN AMUSING GAME UNTIL ILL CHANCE BROUGHT IT TO A PAINFUL END. PLEASE GIVE ME TIME TO EXPLAIN."

1574   © King Features Syndicate, Inc. 1967. World rights reserved.   4-9

"I NEVER WANT TO SEE YOU AGAIN, NEVER! EVEN IF YOU CAME BACK A HUNDRED TIMES I WOULD NOT SPEAK TO YOU....YOU SHEEP IN WOLF'S CLOTHING!"

"COME, REYNOLDE, LET US GET SOME SLEEP, FOR TOMORROW WE MUST FACE OUR HOST AND APOLOGIZE FOR OUR DECEPTION. LET US HOPE WE HAVE WIT ENOUGH TO TURN THEIR CHAGRIN INTO LAUGHTER." NEXT WEEK — Never, almost

HAL FOSTER

Prince Valiant
IN THE DAYS OF KING ARTHUR
BY HAROLD R FOSTER

Our Story: LOVE IS A WONDROUS THING, SO THE POETS TELL US. IT BRINGS ECSTASY AND PAIN, HOPE AND DESPAIR, AND A LARGE AMOUNT OF SELF PITY. PLAIN COMMON SENSE IS NOT ONE OF ITS INGREDIENTS. AFTER A SLEEPLESS NIGHT REYNOLDE GOES IN SEARCH OF ANN.

THE LADY ANN TOO HAS PASSED A RESTLESS NIGHT AND IS IN A SNAPPISH MOOD. SHE LOOKS COLDLY AT HIM AS HE BLUSHES, STAMMERS AND AT LAST BLURTS OUT: "ANN, I LOVE YOU!"

RECEIVING NO REPLY HE STORMS OFF, ENTERS THE TOURNAMENT, AND IS TUMBLED TO THE TURF BY THE FIRST HARDY KNIGHT HE MEETS.

NOT SINCE SHE GAVE UP PLAYING WITH DOLLS HAS ANN SEEN ANYTHING SO IN NEED OF A WOMAN'S CARE AS THIS HAPLESS YOUTH. "ARE YOU HURT?" SHE ASKS ANXIOUSLY. "CERTAINLY I AM!" HE SNAPS. "DO YOU THINK IT WAS A FEATHER PILLOW HE HIT ME WITH?"

"OH, I AM SORRY. YOU MUST BE MORE CAREFUL," SHE ADVISES, NOTICING THAT HE HAS NICE EYES.
"YOU TALK LIKE A MOTHER TO A SMALL CHILD," HE GRUMBLES, "AND I FIND IT UNBECOMING FROM ONE WHO IS BUT A CHILD HERSELF."
"I WILL HAVE GROWN UP ERE YOU RETURN FROM CAMELOT WITH YOUR GOLDEN SPURS," SHE REPLIES.

REYNOLDE IS SO BEFUDDLED IT IS A FULL MINUTE BEFORE HE REALIZES ANN HAS PRACTICALLY INVITED HIM TO RETURN!
"ANN, ANN!" HE CRIES, BUT TOO LATE, SHE HAS GONE.

THE JOUSTING IS OVER FOR THE DAY, AND AS THE GUESTS GATHER IN THE DINING HALL IT IS QUITE EVIDENT THERE HAS BEEN A DECEPTION, FOR THERE IS NO MISTAKING THE REAL PRINCE VALIANT. EVEN THEIR HOST IS ANGRY AT BEING HOODWINKED, AND REYNOLDE WONDERS IF HE WILL EVER BE ABLE TO RETURN.

NEXT WEEK— **The Test**

HAL FOSTER

1575   4-16

Our Story: AT FIRST THE COMPANY IS ANGRY AT BEING DECEIVED, SO PRINCE VALIANT EXPLAINS: "BY CHANCE I FELL IN WITH A TROUPE OF JONGLEURS AND BECAUSE I COULD SING AND PLAY STRINGED INSTRUMENTS, THEY INVITED ME TO JOIN THEIR BAND. I AGREED, FOR THEY WERE A HAPPY CREW AND LIGHTENED THE JOURNEY WITH SONG AND JEST. MY COMPANION, REYNOLDE, I SENT AHEAD."

"WHEN I ARRIVED HE HAD ASSUMED MY CLOTHES AND IDENTITY: 'IT WILL BE FUN TO DINE IN STATE WHILE THE REAL PRINCE VALIANT EATS IN THE KITCHEN AND SLEEPS IN THE STABLE.'"

THEN VAL DESCRIBES THE PRANKS THEY PLAYED, THE RIOTS OF FUN AND FROLIC IN THE KITCHEN. HE SINGS SOME OF THEIR SALTY SONGS AND FROWNS TURN TO SMILES, BUT WHEN HE TELLS THE JOKES HE HEARD THERE ARE ROARS OF LAUGHTER. THE DECEPTION HAS BEEN FORGIVEN.

"WELL, REYNOLDE, IT NOW LOOKS AS IF YOU MAY RETURN WITHOUT THE GATES BEING SHUT IN YOUR FACE." REYNOLDE TURNS IN HIS SADDLE AND LOOKS BACK; A SCARF FLUTTERS FROM THE BATTLEMENTS. "YES," HE SHOUTS GLEEFULLY, "I WILL COME BACK!"

HIS HEART FLUTTERS EVEN MORE THAN THE SCARF. "CAMELOT, HERE I COME!" HE EXCLAIMS, "TO DO GREAT DEEDS AND WIN MANY HONORS TO LAY AT HER FEET AS I ASK FOR THE HAND OF LADY ANN!"

"WE ARE NEARING CAMELOT," SAYS VAL, "SO ARM YOURSELF, FOR ALMOST ANY ADVENTURE IS LIKELY TO HAPPEN ALONG THIS ROAD."

1576

4-23

"YOUR FIRST ADVENTURE LIES AHEAD, FOR I SEE A KNIGHT GUARDING THE CROSS-ROAD. HE WILL, AS IS THE CUSTOM, DEMAND A JOUST. THE HONOR IS YOURS."

NEXT WEEK—Lesson Number One

Prince Valiant
IN THE DAYS OF KING ARTHUR
BY HAROLD R. FOSTER

Our Story: "YONDER KNIGHT IS ONE OF MANY TO BE MET AS WE NEAR CAMELOT. SEEKING A REPUTATION OR PLUNDER THEY CHALLENGE ALL WHO PASS TO A JOUST. HERE IS A CHANCE TO PROVE YOUR METTLE, REYNOLDE."

THE KNIGHT-ERRANT PACES FORWARD: "YIELD TO ME YOUR HORSE AND ARMS," HE GROWLS, "OR CONTEND WITH ME FOR THE RIGHT TO PASS."

VAL WATCHES HIS FRIEND WITH CRITICAL EYE. HIS HORSEMANSHIP IS SUPERB, BUT HE HANDLES SHIELD AND SPEAR LIKE A CLUMSY GOATHERD... AND QUICKLY IS UNHORSED. "YIELD!" BELLOWS THE KNIGHT. "I CLAIM HORSE AND ARMS AS THE PRIZE OF VICTORY."

"NOT SO FAST, SIR KNIGHT," CHIDES VAL. "I TOO HAVE STEED AND ARMS TO RISK IN FAIR FIGHT." THE KNIGHT-ERRANT GLOWERS AT VAL, THEN HIS EXPRESSION CHANGES AS HE RECOGNIZES THE WEARER OF THE CRIMSON STALLION. ALL THE FUN GOES OUT OF JOUSTING AND HE WISHES HE WERE FAR AWAY.

THE RESULT IS AS BAD AS HE EXPECTED, SAVE ONLY THAT THE WINNER REFUSES THE PRIZE OF VICTORY. VAL RETURNS TO THE STILL-DAZED REYNOLDE: "BY THE TWO FACES OF JANUS, HOW CAN ONE RIDE SO WELL ON THE ONE HAND AND BE SO CLUMSY AT ARMS ON THE OTHER?"

"ALL MY LIFE I HAVE BRED FINE HORSES AND KEPT ACCOUNTS OF MY FATHER'S HOLDINGS. THERE HAS BEEN LITTLE TIME TO PRACTICE A WARRIOR'S SKILLS."

"BUT NOW ALL WILL BE CHANGED. AT CAMELOT I WILL LEARN, PRACTICE, AND BECOME A KNIGHT WORTHY TO ASK FOR THE HAND OF FAIR LADY ANN!"

1577 © King Features Syndicate, Inc., 1967. World rights reserved. 4-30

CAMELOT! ITS SOARING TURRETS MATCH THE YOUTHFUL DREAMS OF REYNOLDE. VAL IS SILENT, FOR HE KNOWS WHAT LIES AHEAD FOR THIS GALLANT YOUTH.

NEXT WEEK— Homecoming

1577

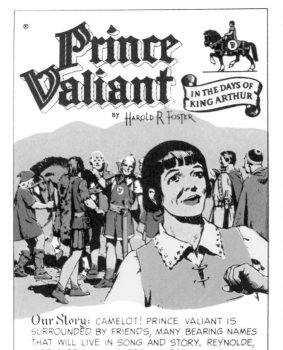

Prince Valiant
IN THE DAYS OF KING ARTHUR
BY HAROLD R FOSTER

Our Story: CAMELOT! PRINCE VALIANT IS SURROUNDED BY FRIENDS, MANY BEARING NAMES THAT WILL LIVE IN SONG AND STORY. REYNOLDE, WIDE-EYED WITH WONDER, WANDERS AIMLESSLY AMID THE SPLENDORS OF THE CASTLE.

VAL GOES TO FIND THE KING AND MAKE HIS REPORT. HE FINDS ARTHUR IN THE EXERCISE YARD PRACTICING THE SKILLS OF BATTLE.

A SMALL KINGDOM HAS BEEN SAVED FROM A RUINOUS CIVIL WAR, A PRINCE FOUND, A KING CROWNED, AND AN OATH OF LOYALTY TO KING ARTHUR OBTAINED.

HIS BUSINESS OVER, VAL IS FREE FOR MORE IMPORTANT THINGS. WHEN THEY WERE QUARTERED WITHIN THE CASTLE THE TWINS WERE EITHER IMPS IN CONSTANT TROUBLE OR LITTLE ANGELS BEING PAMPERED AND SPOILED. SO VAL HAS BOUGHT A HOUSE AND GARDEN IN THE TOWN. NOW, BREATHLESS, HE ARRIVES AT THE DOOR.

ALETA SEEMS LOVELIER THAN EVER AND THE CHILDREN GROWING FAIR AND HEALTHY. SUCH CONTENTMENT COMES SELDOM TO MEN IN HIS PROFESSION, SO VAL WALLOWS IN COMFORT AND AFFECTION... AND POOR REYNOLDE IS ALMOST FORGOTTEN.

HE FINDS HIS WAY TO THE OFFICE OF SIR BALDWIN, THE OFFICER IN CHARGE OF SQUIRES, AND STATES HIS DESIRE TO ENLIST IN THE FELLOWSHIP OF THE ROUND TABLE. SIR BALDWIN EXPLAINS:

1578   5-7

"FIRST YOU MUST PROVE YOUR SKILL AS A NOVICE, THEN AS SQUIRE OR BACHELOR PREPARE FOR COMBAT. SURVIVORS OF THESE TESTS BECOME KNIGHTS-AT-ARMS. THE NEXT STEP IS KNIGHT-WARRIOR, HARDENED IN BATTLE. ONLY THOSE WHO DO GREAT SERVICE TO THE REALM ARE ELECTED TO THE ROUND TABLE."

"WHAT A LONG ROAD LIES AHEAD," PONDERS REYNOLDE, AS HE WENDS HIS WAY TO THE PRACTICE COURT. THERE A BOY AT LEAST FOUR YEARS HIS JUNIOR ASKS BRIGHTLY, "DO YOU WISH TO GO A PRACTICE ROUND?"

NEXT WEEK—The Misfit

Prince Valiant
IN THE DAYS OF KING ARTHUR
BY Harold R. Foster

Our Story: REYNOLDE IS DISAPPOINTED TO LEARN THAT HE CANNOT ENLIST AS A KNIGHT OF THE ROUND TABLE BUT MUST WORK HIS WAY UP. THEN WHEN HE IS ASKED TO FIGHT A PRACTICE ROUND WITH A MERE BOY HIS PRIDE IS HURT.

MORE THAN PRIDE IS HURT FOR THE BOY IS AS ELUSIVE AS THISTLEDOWN, SHARP AS A SWOOPING FALCON. AS REYNOLDE'S ANGER RISES HIS BRUISES MULTIPLY.

"MY COURTESY IS AT FAULT," EXCLAIMS VAL, RISING. "I HAVE NEGLECTED THE CHARMING YOUTH WHO RODE HITHER WITH ME. I GO TO FETCH HIM."

VAL FINDS REYNOLDE IN THE PRACTICE COURT BEING SOUNDLY WHIPPED BY HIS OWN SON ARN! "HALT! ENOUGH!" CALLS THE DRILL SERGEANT. "YOU, BE HERE AT DAWN. YOU WILL HAVE TO START IN THE BEGINNERS' CLASS." THIS IS THE FINAL BLOW TO REYNOLDE'S EGO.

"HELLO, SIRE," CALLS ARN AND "HELLO, SON," ANSWERS VAL. "SO THIS IS THE SON OF PRINCE VALIANT! I MIGHT HAVE KNOWN IT!" AND, NODDING TO ARN, REYNOLDE SAYS: "THANK YOU FOR SO THOROUGHLY WHACKING THE DUST FROM MY PADDING."

ALETA FINDS REYNOLDE CHARMING. HE IS SO FULL OF BOYISH DREAMS. ONLY WHEN HE TALKS ABOUT HORSES DOES HE COME DOWN FROM THE CLOUDS AND SHOW THAT HE HAS A FINE KNOWLEDGE OF HIS SUBJECT.

5-14-67

"THERE GOES A TRAGEDY," REMARKS VAL. "THAT LAD IS SO INEPT HE COULD NOT HIT A HAYSTACK WITH A BROOMSTICK, YET HE HAS COURAGE AND WILL FALL IN HIS FIRST BATTLE."

ANOTHER YOUTH WHO WILL NEVER BECOME THE WARRIOR HE HAD HOPED TO BE IS SAILING UP THE CHANNEL TOWARD CAMELOT. HE HAS BUT ONE LEG.

NEXT WEEK—The Arrival of Geoffrey

1579

Prince Valiant
IN THE DAYS OF KING ARTHUR
BY Harold R Foster

Our Story: A YOUNG MAN ARRIVES IN CAMELOT AND GAZES WIDE-EYED ON THE SPLENDORS THAT ONCE WERE SO FAMILIAR TO HIM. HERE HE HAD DREAMED OF DOING SUCH WONDROUS DEEDS AS WOULD EARN HIM A SEAT AT THE ROUND TABLE.

"CAN YOU TELL ME WHERE I MAY FIND PRINCE VALIANT?" HE ASKS A DESPONDENT YOUTH. *"I WILL TAKE YOU TO HIM,"* ANSWERS REYNOLDE, *"FOR HE IS A FRIEND OF MINE."*

AND SO GEOFFREY, SCRIBE AND HISTORIAN, COMES ONCE AGAIN INTO THE HOME WHERE HE, A RUNAWAY BOY, LEARNED OF LOVE AND LAUGHTER, COURAGE AND THE FORTITUDE THAT CARRIED HIM THROUGH THE AWFUL DAYS WHEN HE LOST HIS LEG.

ALETA SURVEYS HER HOUSE GUESTS. AS USUAL VAL HAS BEFRIENDED THE INEPT, THE GALLANT MISFIT, THE HIGH-HEARTED YOUTH WITH IMPOSSIBLE DREAMS. GEOFFREY HAD BEEN SUCH A LAD AND WHEN THE LOSS OF HIS LEG DASHED HIS AMBITIONS, VAL HAD USED HIS BOOK-LEARNING AND MADE HIM HISTORIAN OF THULE. NOW THERE IS REYNOLDE.

GENTLE REYNOLDE, BATTERED AND BRUISED FROM HIS CONSTANT PRACTICING, YET STRIVING TO BECOME A WARRIOR WORTHY TO ASK FOR THE HAND OF THE LADY ANN.

A MONTH HAS PASSED BUT ANN WAITS PATIENTLY, FOR SHE IS SURE HE WILL SOON RETURN IN SHINING ARMOR AND LOADED WITH HONORS TO LAY AT HER FEET.

VAL IS WATCHING REYNOLDE AT PRACTICE WITH THE OTHER YOUNG SQUIRES WHEN THE KING STEPS TO HIS SIDE: *"WHAT SUPERB HORSEMANSHIP AND WHAT A SPLENDID MOUNT. WHO IS HE, SIR VAL?"*
"THAT IS REYNOLDE, SON OF SIR HUGO OF DINMORE, AND THE HORSE IS OF HIS OWN BREEDING. BUT, ALAS, SAVE FOR HIS COURAGE, HE HAS NOT THE GIFTS THAT MAKE A WARRIOR. HE WILL NOT SURVIVE HIS FIRST BATTLE."

5-21

1580

A NOVICE IS HAVING TROUBLE WITH HIS HORSE. WITH CRUEL JERKING AT THE BIT AND RAKING OF SPURS HE IS TRYING TO BRING IT UNDER CONTROL. TO VAL'S SURPRISE, GENTLE REYNOLDE SHOUTS: *"SENSELESS FOOL, DO YOU WISH TO BREAK THE SPIRIT OF A FINE HORSE?"*

NEXT WEEK— **The Duel**

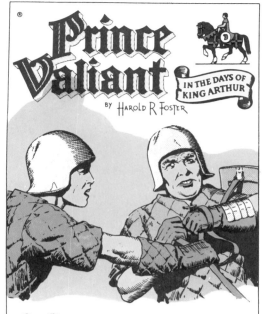

Prince Valiant
IN THE DAYS OF KING ARTHUR
BY Harold R Foster

Our Story: REYNOLDE, USUALLY SO GENTLE, FLIES INTO A RAGE WHEN ONE OF THE YOUNG SQUIRES IS CRUEL TO HIS MOUNT. WORDS ARE SPOKEN IN ANGER, TEMPERS FLARE.

THOUGH EACH IS ARMED WITH WOODEN PRACTICE WEAPONS, ANGER LENDS POWER TO THEIR STROKES. REYNOLDE'S FINE HORSEMANSHIP GIVES HIM A GREAT ADVANTAGE. ONLY HIS CLUMSINESS WITH WEAPONS PREVENTS QUICK VICTORY.

THEN HIS ADVERSARY PUTS CRUEL SPURS TO HIS MOUNT AND IT FLINCHES AWAY, LEAVING AN OPENING THAT EVEN REYNOLDE CANNOT MISS. IT IS HIS FIRST VICTORY.

"DO YOU WISH TO BREAK THE SPIRIT OF THIS FINE HORSE? ARE YOU SO MEAN OF SOUL THAT YOU WOULD MASTER IT THROUGH CRUELTY? LOOK AT THAT BRIDLE, DRAWN SO TIGHT THE BIT HAS DRAWN BLOOD. THE SPURS YOU WEAR ARE MORE LIKE WEAPONS!"

THEN, HIS LECTURE ENDED, REYNOLDE ADJUSTS THE HARNESS AND MOUNTS. WITH FIRM BUT GENTLE HANDS HE SOON CALMS THE HORSE AND THEREAFTER PUTS IT THROUGH ITS PACES.
"BRING YOUR YOUNG FRIEND TO ME, VAL," SAYS THE KING. *"WE HAVE NEED OF SUCH A MAN."*

THE KING TELLS OF THEIR NEED FOR HORSES, HORSES AND MORE HORSES, AND REYNOLDE, HIS FACE ALIGHT WITH ENTHUSIASM, TELLS OF HIS SUCCESS IN BREEDING STRONG, SWIFT MOUNTS, AND HOW THE SAME COULD BE DONE HERE IN CAMELOT. THE SUN SINKS ERE HE IS FINISHED.

5-28

1581

"WILL HE GIVE UP HIS DREAM OF BECOMING A GREAT WARRIOR AND BE CONTENT TO IMPROVE OUR STOCK?" ASKS THE KING.
"NO, SIRE," ANSWERS VAL. *"A PRETTY GIRL IS INVOLVED."* ARTHUR NODS SADLY. THERE IS ALWAYS A GIRL SOMEWHERE TO UPSET ONE'S PLANS.

NEXT WEEK—**Despair**

Our Story: YOUNG REYNOLDE OF DINMORE NEVER KNEW OF THE ANXIETY HE CAUSED HIS FRIENDS AS THEY WATCHED HIS FUTILE EFFORTS TO ACQUIRE A WARRIOR'S SKILLS. PRINCE ARN KNOWS HIS STRUGGLES TO BE FRUITLESS. GEOFFREY HAD ONCE BURNED WITH THE SAME AMBITION AND IN FAILURE TURNED TO HIS OTHER TALENTS AND BECAME FAMOUS AS SCRIBE AND HISTORIAN. VAL AND ALETA CAN ONLY WAIT. KING ARTHUR IS IN NEED OF REYNOLDE'S GREAT SKILL IN BREEDING FINE HORSES.

THEN THE INEVITABLE HAPPENS AND REYNOLDE IS CARRIED FROM THE PRACTICE LISTS WITH CRACKED BONES AND STRAINED TENDONS.

FOR A WHILE EVERYONE IS HAPPY. REYNOLDE IS ONCE MORE WITH THE BELOVED HORSES AND ARTHUR IS AMAZED AT HIS KNOWLEDGE, AND STRAIGHTWAY ORDERS THAT HIS CRITICISM AND ADVICE BE CARRIED OUT.

ALL GOES WELL AS LONG AS THE KING IS PRESENT, BUT THE CARE OF THE MOUNTS HAS LONG BEEN GIVEN TO KNIGHTS WHOSE YEARS OR WOUNDS HAVE MADE THEM UNFIT FOR BATTLE, AND THEY RESENT THE INTERFERENCE OF AN UNTITLED YOUTH. HIS SUGGESTIONS ARE UNHEEDED.

ANOTHER FAILURE! IN DEEP DESPAIR HE THINKS OF THE LADY ANN WHO IS PATIENTLY AWAITING HIS RETURN AS A FULL-FLEDGED KNIGHT LOADED WITH HONORS. AT THIS MOMENT SHE SEEMS FAR, FAR AWAY.

6-4   © King Features Syndicate, Inc., 1967. World rights reserved   1582

HE HAS TO POUR OUT HIS MISERY TO SOMEONE AND ALETA IS A SYMPATHETIC LISTENER: "AND SO IT SEEMS THAT YEARS WILL PASS ERE I BECOME WORTHY OF HER. WHAT SHALL I DO?"
"ASK HER," ANSWERS ALETA SIMPLY.

"JUST LIKE A WOMAN!" MUTTERS REYNOLDE. "THEY NEVER STOP TO THINK. THE PROBLEM IS NOT THAT SIMPLE..... OR IS IT?"

NEXT WEEK— Aleta Takes Charge

Prince Valiant

IN THE DAYS OF KING ARTHUR

BY HAROLD R. FOSTER

Our Story: REYNOLDE IS SUCH A GENTLE, HELPLESS SORT OF YOUTH THAT HE AROUSES THE MATERNAL INSTINCT IN ALETA. WOMAN-LIKE, SHE SETS ABOUT REARRANGING HIS LIFE.

BEING A QUEEN, BEAUTIFUL AND SPOILED, SHE HAS NO HESITATION IN TELLING THE KING OF ALL THE BRITONS JUST WHAT HE SHOULD DO. AND THE KING, HAVING HAD DEALINGS WITH THIS SMALL BLONDE BEFORE, LISTENS INTENTLY.

"YOU NEED REYNOLDE'S TALENTS. REYNOLDE WANTS TO BE A WARRIOR KNIGHT TO WIN THE LADY ANN. THE LADY ANN HAS NOTIONS OF ROMANCE, OF DARING DEEDS BY KNIGHTS IN SHINING ARMOR. CURE THOSE NOTIONS AND EVERYTHING WILL FALL NEATLY INTO PLACE. NOW, SIRE, HERE IS WHAT WE MUST DO........"

REYNOLDE IS SUMMONED BEFORE THE KING. "WE HEAR THAT ON YOUR FATHER'S FIEF AT DINMORE THERE ARE MANY FINE HORSES SUCH AS THE ONE YOU RIDE. NOW, WE ARE IN NEED OF A FRESH LINE OF BREEDING STOCK. CAN YOU SUPPLY OUR NEEDS?"
"I LEAVE AT DAWN TO DISCUSS THE SALE WITH MY FATHER, SIR HUGO," SAYS REYNOLDE, WHO SEEMS TO GROW IN STATURE WHEN HORSES ARE MENTIONED.

"BY YOUR LEAVE I WILL JOIN YOU ON YOUR JOURNEY," REQUESTS GEOFFREY. REYNOLDE READILY AGREES, FLATTERED THAT SO LEARNED A MAN WOULD WISH HIS COMPANY.

AT TIMES REYNOLDE IS ENTHUSIASTIC AS HE PLANS THE FUTURE OF THE STOCK AT CAMELOT. AT OTHER TIMES HE IS IN DESPAIR WHEN HE THINKS OF THE HOPELESSNESS OF WINNING ANN.

1583

AT A CROSSROAD THEY MEET A KNIGHT, NOW BUT THE WRECKAGE OF MANY BATTLES, MAKING HIS WAY HOMEWARD WITH ONLY HIS SCARS TO SHOW FOR HIS LIFE'S WORK.

6-11 © King Features Syndicate, Inc., 1967. World rights reserved

"SUCH WOULD HAVE BEEN MY FATE HAD I NOT LOST A LEG," SAYS GEOFFREY.
"YOU, A FAMOUS SCRIBE, ASPIRED TO BE A WARRIOR?" ASKS REYNOLDE.
"YES, EVEN AS YOU DO NOW. WOULD YOU LIKE TO HEAR MY STORY?"
NEXT WEEK– A Glance Backward

Prince Valiant
IN THE DAYS OF KING ARTHUR
BY HAROLD R FOSTER

Our Story: *"I FIND IT HARD TO BELIEVE THAT YOU, A FAMOUS SCRIBE AND HISTORIAN, AT ONE TIME SOUGHT TO BECOME A WARRIOR,"* SAYS A PUZZLED REYNOLDE.
"YES, I HAD SUCH ROMANTIC NOTIONS," SMILES GEOFFREY, *"BUT LET ME TELL YOU MY STORY."*

"WHEN I WAS A BOY I RAN AWAY FROM AN UNHAPPY HOME TO SEEK MY FORTUNE, AND IT WAS MY GOOD LUCK TO MEET WITH PRINCE VALIANT, WHO TOOK ME WITH HIM TO CAMELOT."

"THE LADY ALETA BECAME MY INSPIRATION. HER VERY PRESENCE COMMANDED COURTESY, NEATNESS AND A DESIRE TO BE WORTHY OF HER FRIENDSHIP. SHE HAD ME LEARN READING AND WRITING."

"AT FIRST I STUDIED TO PLEASE MY LADY, BUT THE MORE I LEARNED THE MORE I HUNGERED FOR KNOWLEDGE. SIR VALIANT MADE ME HIS SQUIRE AND WE HAD MANY ADVENTURES TOGETHER."

"THEN KING ARTHUR SUMMONED US FOR AN IMPORTANT MISSION, TO RIDE OVERLAND TO ROME ON A ROAD MADE PERILOUS BY MIGRATING GOTHS."

"WE SURVIVED MANY DANGERS AND CAME AT LAST TO THE ALPS AND GAZED UP AT THE MENACING PEAKS WE MUST CROSS TO REACH ROME."

"WE CHOSE ST. BERNARD'S PASS AS OUR CROSSING AND STRUGGLED UPWARD AS FAST AS WE COULD WHILE THE GOOD WEATHER HELD."

6-18   © King Features Syndicate, Inc., 1967. World rights reserved.   1584

"THAT NIGHT CLOUDS BLOTTED OUT THE STARS, AND THE WIND MOANED AMONG THE CRAGS. THEN CAME THE SNOW AND THE ICY GALE ROSE TO A SHRIEK. MY TIME OF TORMENT HAD BEGUN."
NEXT WEEK—*Hour of Despair*

HAL FOSTER

Our Story: GEOFFREY PACES UP AND DOWN AS HE RECOUNTS THE STORY OF HIS ORDEAL, A TRAGEDY THAT DASHED ALL HOPE OF HIS BECOMING A WARRIOR.

"THAT TERRIBLE NIGHT ENDED AT LAST, AND AS WE STRUGGLED FROM THE DRIFTED SNOW I BECAME AWARE THAT MY FEET WERE FROZEN!"

"THE JOURNEY DOWN THE MOUNTAIN WAS A LONG AGONY, BUT MY COMPANIONS FINALLY GOT ME TO TORINO AND PLACED ME IN THE HOSPICE. THEN THEY LEFT TO COMPLETE THEIR MISSION."

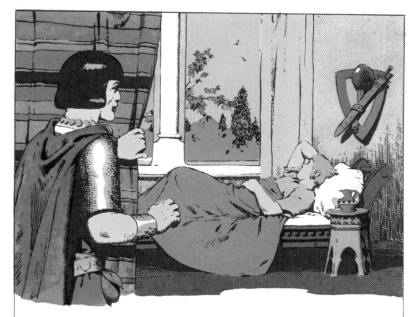

"I LOST MY LEG. GONE WAS THE SPLENDID DREAM OF KNIGHTHOOD. I LOST EVEN THE WILL TO LIVE. THEN PRINCE VALIANT RETURNED AND I POURED OUT MY TALE OF WOE: 'MY SWORD AND SHIELD ARE USELESS NOW AND SO AM I. THIS IS THE END.'"

"NOT SO," PRINCE VALIANT SAID. "THIS IS THE BEGINNING. THE LADY ALETA AND I HAVE TAUGHT YOU TO READ AND WRITE. YOU WILL FIND THE PEN AND INKHORN MORE SUITED TO YOUR GIFTS THAN SWORD OR SHIELD. I HAVE KNOWN FOR A LONG TIME THAT NATURE HAD NOT EQUIPPED YOU TO BE A WARRIOR."

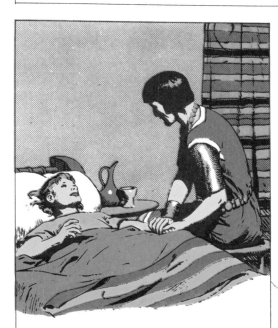

"NOW YOU HAVE WORK TO DO. HERE ARE THE NOTES I MADE OF OUR MISSION. WRITE THEM OUT CLEARLY AND IN DETAIL THAT THEY MAY BE SENT TO KING ARTHUR ADVISING HIM OF OUR SUCCESS."

DARKNESS COMES AS GEOFFREY CONCLUDES HIS TALE, BUT REYNOLDE SITS LONG IN THOUGHT. COULD IT BE THAT THE MORAL OF THIS TALE REFERS TO HIM TOO? AFTER ALL HIS STRUGGLES AND DEFEATS IS HE ALSO TO FAIL AS A WARRIOR? NEVER HAS HE KNOWN SUCH DEEP DESPAIR

NEXT WEEK — The Rival

1585   6-25

Prince Valiant

IN THE DAYS OF KING ARTHUR

BY Harold R Foster

Our Story: GEOFFREY ENDS HIS TALE AND, WRAPPED SNUGLY IN HIS CLOAK, GOES TO SLEEP. BUT REYNOLDE STARES LONG INTO THE FIRE. COULD THE TALE RELATE TO HIM, IS HE ONE OF THOSE UNFORTUNATES WHO WILL NEVER BECOME A GREAT WARRIOR?

"GEOFFREY FAILED AT ARMS BUT HE HAD OTHER TALENTS, A POET, HISTORIAN AND SCRIBE, WHILE I.......I CAN BE NOTHING BUT A GLORIFIED STABLEBOY!......

.....AND THE LADY ANN, SHE TOLD ME SHE WOULD AWAIT UNTIL I RETURNED WEARING THE GOLDEN SPURS OF KNIGHTHOOD. CAN SHE WAIT FOREVER?"

AS THEY NEAR GLENHAVEN REYNOLDE WANTS TO RIDE ON BY, FOR HE IS ASHAMED TO FACE ANN, BUT GEOFFREY REMINDS HIM THAT THEY MUST RETURN THIS WAY WITH THE HORSES, AND ARRANGEMENTS MUST BE MADE FOR CORRAL AND FODDER.

ONCE MORE ANN AND REYNOLDE COME FACE TO FACE AND, AS THEY ARE QUITE YOUNG AND IN LOVE, IT IS NOT TO BE EXPECTED THAT THEY ARE ALWAYS RATIONAL. TO PLEASE HIM SHE RATTLES ON ABOUT CAMELOT, KNIGHTS AND DEEDS OF CHIVALRY AND HE, KNOWING THESE ROMANTIC THINGS ARE NOT FOR HIM, IS SILENT AND ALOOF.

TO ADD TO HIS DESPAIR REYNOLDE HAS A RIVAL, SIR BALA LLANWYN, A MUSCULAR YOUTH WHO WEARS, CONSTANTLY, A MEDALLION THAT PROCLAIMS HIM CHAMPION OF A MINOR TOURNAMENT. AND AS HE TELLS OF HIS FINE DEEDS WITH LANCE AND SWORD REYNOLDE ENVIES HIM AND ANN IS SPELLBOUND.

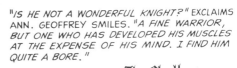

"IS HE NOT A WONDERFUL KNIGHT?" EXCLAIMS ANN. GEOFFREY SMILES. "A FINE WARRIOR, BUT ONE WHO HAS DEVELOPED HIS MUSCLES AT THE EXPENSE OF HIS MIND. I FIND HIM QUITE A BORE."

NEXT WEEK—The Challenge

1586

7-2

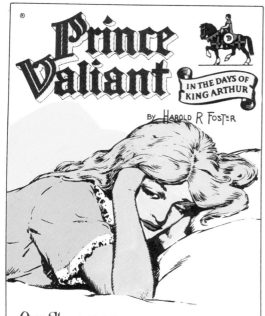

Prince Valiant

IN THE DAYS OF KING ARTHUR

BY HAROLD R FOSTER

Our Story: IN ALL HER SEVENTEEN YEARS ANN HAS NEVER KNOWN SUCH MISERY. SHE HAS BEEN AS NICE AS COULD BE TO REYNOLDE, BUT HE HAS REBUFFED HER. HIS COLDNESS HAS BROKEN HER HEART FOREVER.

IN DEEP DESPAIR REYNOLDE GAZES INTO THE MOONLIT GARDEN: *"ANN, ANN,"* HE MOANS, *"HOW CAN YOU EVER LOOK AT ME AGAIN WHEN I FALL SO FAR BELOW YOUR IDEALS?"* THEN HE REMEMBERS HAVING SAID THE SAME THING TO LADY ALETA AND SHE HAD SAID, *"THAT'S SIMPLE, ASK HER."* WHY NOT?

HE SEEKS HER OUT NEXT MORNING AND IN A DULL, DISCOURAGED VOICE SAYS; *"I LOVE YOU, ANN. HAVE I YOUR PERMISSION TO ASK YOUR PARENTS FOR YOUR HAND?"* *"YES!"* SHE YELLS GRABBING HIS ARM.

HIS RIVAL, SIR BALA LLANWYN, IS THERE FOR THE SAME PURPOSE, AND AN ARGUMENT BEGINS. ANN'S MOTHER FAVORS REYNOLDE AS BEING MORE GENTEEL AND SCHOOLED, BUT HER FATHER HOLDS OUT FOR BALA. *"IF WE HAVE TO PUT UP WITH A SON-IN-LAW, IT IS BETTER TO HAVE ONE WHO CAN FIGHT IN CASE OF NEED."*

THE ARGUMENT GOES ON FAR INTO THE NIGHT, BUT NO ONE KNOWS HOW IT CAME OUT OR WHO WON. THOUGH THE VOICES ARE LOUD THE BEDROOM DOORS ARE THICK.

"BUT ONE OF US CAN WED WITH OUR LADY ANN. IT IS INCONCEIVABLE THAT THE OTHER WOULD WISH TO LIVE WITHOUT HER." *"HOW HAPPILY YOU SOLVE THESE PROBLEMS,"* ANSWERS REYNOLDE. *"I RETURN IN TWO WEEKS, AND BY THAT TIME MY SHIELD ARM SHOULD BE MENDED, MY SWORD SHARPENED."*

REYNOLDE CONTINUES ON HIS WAY TO DINMORE THROUGH FORESTS MADE BRIGHT WITH AUTUMN COLORS.

ANN DREAMS PLEASANTLY OF THE DAY WHEN REYNOLDE WILL BE HERS TO GUIDE, PET, BULLY, CARE FOR, LOVE AND MAKE HAPPY. EVEN THE NOISE OF BALA WHACKING A DUMMY IN THE PRACTICE YARD IN PREPARATION FOR THE COMING DUEL CANNOT DISTURB THOSE DREAMS.

NEXT WEEK — *The Roundup*

7-9

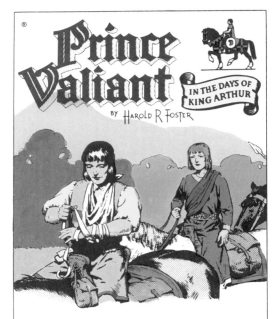

Prince Valiant

IN THE DAYS OF KING ARTHUR
BY Harold R Foster

Our Story: WHEN THEIR JOURNEY TO DINMORE IS RESUMED REYNOLDE REMOVES THE SLING AND BANDAGE FROM HIS INJURED ARM. ALTHOUGH IT IS PAINFUL HE CARRIES HIS SHIELD, TRYING BY EXERCISE TO REGAIN THE LOST STRENGTH.

IT IS NOT LONG BEFORE GEOFFREY LEARNS OF THE COMING DUEL WITH BALA. IT IS A MATTER OF HONOR FROM WHICH THERE CAN BE NO DRAWING BACK.

"THERE LIES MY FATHER'S FIEF, THE FAIREST MEADOWS IN ALL THE LAND. WE HAVE BRED A FINE STRAIN OF HORSES THAT WILL SOON MAKE ARTHUR'S CAVALRY THE BEST-MOUNTED IN THE WORLD!"

SIR HUGO WELCOMES HIS SON AND WOULD GLADLY HAVE THE REUNION A PRETEXT FOR A CELEBRATION, BUT REYNOLDE IS EAGER TO MAKE A SUCCESS OF THIS, HIS FIRST MISSION FOR HIS KING.

HORSES MUST BE SELECTED, GROOMS AND RIDERS PICKED, A ROUTE CHOSEN THAT WILL PROVIDE PASTURE. "YOU HAVE DONE WELL, REYNOLDE, AND BROUGHT A PROSPERITY TO OUR FIEF WE HAVE NEVER KNOWN. WE CAN INCREASE OUR PASTURE LAND AND HERD. THE KING, I AM SURE, WILL WANT MANY MORE OF OUR STEEDS."

LOOKING FROM HER WINDOW ANN IS AWARE THAT A HERD OF FINE-LOOKING HORSES IS BEING LED INTO THE CORRAL, BUT HER EYES ARE ONLY FOR REYNOLDE.

"AS YOU KNOW, GEOFFREY, I HAVE A MATTER TO SETTLE WITH BALA LLANWYN, AND SHOULD I MEET WITH MISFORTUNE YOU ARE TO SEE THE HORSES SAFELY TO CAMELOT. HERE ARE THE PAPERS, PRICES, TITLES AND ALL. I LEAVE THEM IN YOUR CARE."

BALA ALSO SEES THE ARRIVAL AND GOES TO SHARPEN HIS SWORD.

NEXT WEEK—The King's Mission

7-16   © King Features Syndicate, Inc., 1967. World rights reserved   1588

Prince Valiant

IN THE DAYS OF KING ARTHUR
BY HAROLD R FOSTER

Our Story: THERE CAN BE LITTLE DOUBT THAT REYNOLDE WILL NOT SURVIVE HIS DUEL WITH BALA, YET HE SHOWS NO SIGN OF FEAR. GEOFFREY ADMIRES HIS COURAGE AND MAKES SOME PLANS OF HIS OWN.

REYNOLDE GREETS THE LADY ANN AND HER PARENTS CHEERFULLY, AND IF HE GAZES INTO HER EYES FOR A LONG MOMENT IT IS BECAUSE HE SUSPECTS THIS MAY BE THE LAST TIME.

AFTER MAKING ARRANGEMENTS FOR THE PASTURING OF HIS HORSES AND QUARTERS FOR THE HERDSMEN, HE GOES TO ARM HIMSELF. BALA, HE KNOWS, WILL BE IMPATIENT.

IN A SECLUDED CORNER OF THE COURTYARD THEY DRESS THEIR SHIELDS. "PUT UP YOUR SWORDS, THERE WILL BE NO DUELING," SAYS GEOFFREY QUIETLY, STEPPING BETWEEN THEM. "REYNOLDE IS ON A MISSION FOR THE KING AND THE KING DOES NOT DEAL KINDLY WITH THOSE WHO HINDER HIS PLANS."

"BUT THIS IS A MATTER OF HONOR!" BLUSTERS BALA. "HONOR!" MOCKS GEOFFREY. "YOU ARE BUT A WANDERING KNIGHT FIGHTING FOR PROFIT AND A REPUTATION, A PROFESSIONAL BULLY. IF YOU WANT HONOR GO TO CAMELOT AND TAKE PRIDE IN FIGHTING FOR A WORTH-WHILE CAUSE."

HAL FOSTER

BALA IS VERY QUIET THIS EVENING AND BY THE FURROWS ON HIS BROW IT WOULD SEEM HE IS THINKING. ALL HIS LIFE HE HAS BELIEVED THAT STRENGTH AND FIGHTING SKILL ARE ALL THAT IS IMPORTANT. YET HERE ARE TWO MEN HE COULD CRUSH WITH LITTLE EFFORT AND THEY MAKE HIM FEEL LIKE AN IGNORANT BOY. COULD IT BE TRUE THAT BRAINS ARE BETTER THAN BRAWN?

7-23

1589

"GO TO CAMELOT? NO! I AM NOW FREE TO FIGHT WHEN AND WHOM I PLEASE. DEVELOP A BRAIN? BOSH! IT ONLY MAKES ONE TALK STRANGELY AND ENDLESSLY, A BORE."

NEXT WEEK—Heart and Hand

Prince Valiant

IN THE DAYS OF KING ARTHUR

BY HAROLD R. FOSTER

Our Story: REYNOLDE IS UP WITH THE DAWN AND ON HIS WAY TO THE MEADOWS TO SEE THAT HIS BELOVED HORSES ARE WELL CARED FOR AND RESTED, FOR IT IS STILL A LONG RIDE TO CAMELOT.
THEN THERE IS ANOTHER ITEM OF MAJOR IMPORTANCE. ALTHOUGH THE LADY ANN HAS GIVEN HIM HER HEART, IT IS HER PARENTS WHO MUST GIVE HER HAND.

THAT BUSINESS IS BEING SETTLED. "I THINK WE SHOULD CONSIDER BALA AS A SON-IN-LAW. HE IS A STOUT FELLOW AND HANDY TO HAVE AROUND IN CASE OF TROUBLE," ANNOUNCES THE FATHER.

"IF THERE IS TROUBLE IT WILL BE OF HIS MAKING," ANSWERS THE MOTHER, "FOR ALL HE THINKS ABOUT IS FIGHTING. HE WILL NOT BE WORTH HIS KEEP AS HE DOES NOT KNOW ENOUGH TO SUPERINTEND THE FIEF."

"ON THE OTHER HAND REYNOLDE HAS THE KING'S FAVOR AND THE SALE OF HIS HORSES WILL BRING GREAT WEALTH.
AND, IN CASE OF TROUBLE, WE WILL BE BOUND TO SIR HUGH'S FIEF AT DUNMORE BY BONDS OF MARRIAGE AND CAN EXPECT HELP FROM THAT QUARTER."

SIR BALA IS FURIOUS. HE IS DENIED A PRETTY WIFE, A COMFORTABLE PLACE TO LIVE FREE, AND THEN, WHO KNOWS, HE MIGHT SOME DAY HAVE INHERITED THE FIEF!

1590   © King Features Syndicate, Inc., 1967. World rights reserved.   7-30

THE HORSES ARE ROUNDED UP. HERDERS TAKE THEIR PLACES AND THE RIDE TO CAMELOT BEGINS. THEN, TO THE SURPRISE OF EVERYONE, BALA ASKS IF HE MAY JOIN THEM.
"YES, AND WELCOME," ANSWERS REYNOLDE, "FOR WE NEED ALL THE RIDERS WE CAN GET TO KEEP THE HERD TOGETHER."

NEXT WEEK— *Help or Revenge?*

Prince Valiant
IN THE DAYS OF KING ARTHUR
BY Harold R Foster

Our Story: SIR BALA JOINS THE DRIVE TO BRING REYNOLDE'S HERD OF HORSES TO CAMELOT, NOT TO DO ANY USEFUL WORK, BUT TO SEEK A CHANCE FOR REVENGE ON HIS SUCCESSFUL RIVAL.

MANY YOUNG MEN OF NOBLE FAMILIES ARE HELPING IN THE DRIVE, AND THIS SURPRISES BALA, WHO HAS BELIEVED FIGHTING THE ONLY OCCUPATION FOR A MAN.

GEOFFREY RIDES AHEAD TO TELL OF THEIR COMING AND MAKE PREPARATIONS FOR THE HORSES.

REYNOLDE KNEW HE HAD BRED A FINE STRAIN OF MOUNTS, BUT HE HAD NO IDEA HOW IMPORTANT THEY WERE TO ARTHUR'S CAVALRY. THE KING AND MANY FAMOUS KNIGHTS ARE AT THE CORRALS TO WELCOME THEIR ARRIVAL.

IF BALA EXPECTED THE GREAT WARRIOR KNIGHTS TO BE TALL, MUSCULAR, FROWNING BULLIES, READY TO FIGHT AT A WORD, HE IS MISTAKEN. THE MORE FAMOUS THE KNIGHT THE MORE COURTEOUS HE IS. THESE PEOPLE MAKE HIM FEEL LIKE AN UNCOUTH YOKEL.

AND ABOUT THIS TIME PRINCE VALIANT FEELS HE HAS BEEN RESTED LONG ENOUGH, SO HE HANGS HIS SHIELD IN THE HALL OF CHAMPIONS, A SIGN THAT HE IS PRESENT AND READY FOR DUTY.

"JUST IN TIME," SMILES ARTHUR. "WE HAVE A BIT OF REPAIR WORK FOR YOU. IT SHOULD NOT TAKE LONG AND YOU WILL BE BACK FOR THE HUNTING SEASON."

1591   © King Features Syndicate, Inc., 1967. World rights reserved   8-6

HAL FOSTER

"EARL CLIVE OF WICKWAIN HAS DIED AND HIS HALF BROTHER LAYS CLAIM TO THE LANDS AS NEXT IN LINE OF SUCCESSION. THE WIDOW REFUTES THE CLAIM. GO STRAIGHTEN THE MATTER OUT BEFORE A BLOOD FEUD BEGINS."

NEXT WEEK – **The New Squire**

Prince Valiant
IN THE DAYS OF KING ARTHUR
BY HAROLD R FOSTER

Our Story: "THE WIDOW OF EARL CLIVE AND HER DAUGHTER SEEM TO HAVE THE BEST CLAIM ON THE FIEF," EXPLAINS ARTHUR, "BUT THE HALF-BROTHER, SLIGOL, ALSO DEMANDS HIS RIGHTS. GO TO WICKWAIN AND EXAMINE THEIR RECORDS."

IT IS CUSTOMARY FOR EXPERIENCED KNIGHTS TO TAKE ONE OF THE YOUNGER ONES ALONG FOR TRAINING. SIR BALDWIN, IN CHARGE OF RECRUITS, ASSIGNS BALA TO VAL.

VAL TELLS OF THEIR MISSION AND WHAT THEY HOPE TO ACCOMPLISH, BUT BALA IS NOT INTERESTED. ALL HE WANTS TO KNOW IS WHETHER THERE WILL BE FIGHTING AND WHAT THE SPOILS MIGHT BE.

OH, YES -- REYNOLDE! WELL, THE KING EVENTUALLY MADE HIM KNIGHT-CUSTODIAN-OF-HORSE, AND HE RODE HAPPILY OUT OF OUR STORY ON HIS WAY TO CLAIM THE HAND OF LADY ANN, AND THEY MIGHT HAVE LIVED HAPPILY EVER AFTER THOUGH THEY WERE WED IN THE SPRING.

IT IS A HOT AFTERNOON AND THE POOL LOOKS INVITING. "I SHALL TAKE A SWIM," SAYS VAL. "WILL YOU JOIN ME?" BUT BALA SHRUGS DISDAINFULLY AND RIDES ON.

VAL FINDS HIS COMPANION IN A GLADE. BALA IS DRAWING HIS SWORD AS HE WALKS TOWARD A LIMP FIGURE ON THE SWARD, EVIDENTLY THE LOSER OF A JOUST.

"I AM NOEL, NEPHEW OF THE LATE EARL OF CLIVE, ON MY WAY TO SEEK THE KING'S JUSTICE," SAYS THE INJURED YOUTH. "WE HAVE BEEN SENT TO BRING THAT JUSTICE," ANSWERS VAL.

8-13 © King Features Syndicate, Inc. 1967. World rights reserved. 1592

"HIS HORSE AND ARMS ARE MINE, WON IN FAIR FIGHT!" BLUSTERS BALA. THERE IS CONTEMPT IN VAL'S VOICE: "YOU DO NOT KNOW THE DIFFERENCE BETWEEN KNIGHTLY CONDUCT AND ARMED ROBBERY!"

NEXT WEEK- **To Have and to Hold**

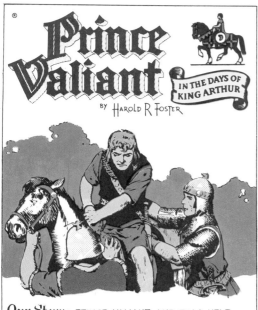

Prince Valiant
IN THE DAYS OF KING ARTHUR
BY HAROLD R FOSTER

Our Story: PRINCE VALIANT AND BALA HELP NOEL TO THE SADDLE. THE BOY IS UNHURT BUT BRUISED AND SHAKEN. BALA IS PUZZLED. HE WANTS TO BECOME ONE OF THE KING'S KNIGHTS BUT HE CANNOT UNDERSTAND THEIR UNPROFITABLE IDEALS.

VAL CONTROLS HIS ANGER: *"WE ARE ON A MISSION FOR OUR KING. WE FIGHT ONLY THOSE WHO WOULD OBSTRUCT US. NOEL WAS SEEKING THE KING'S JUSTICE AND SHOULD BE HELPED, NOT HINDERED!"*

AS THEY RIDE TOWARD WICKWAIN, NOEL TELLS OF HOW SLIGOL HAD CLAIMED IT AS HIS HERITAGE AND MOVED IN WITH AN ARMED TROOP.

THE FAIR FIELDS OF WICKWAIN LIE UNTENDED, THE WALLS GRIM AND SILENT, SENTRIES STANDING AT THE READY. BEFORE THE OAKEN GATES VAL HALTS; *"OPEN IN THE KING'S NAME!"* AFTER A LONG WAIT AND MUCH WRANGLING THE PORTALS CREAK OPEN.

ARMED MEN ARE EVERYWHERE. COWED SERFS TAKE THEIR HORSES. THE GUARDS AT THE DOOR FALL BACK GRUDGINGLY BEFORE THE ANGRY MENACE OF SIR VALIANT'S EYE.

SLIGOL IS SEATED AT A TABLE STREWN WITH DOCUMENTS. *"YOU ARE NOT WELCOME HERE. I HOLD THIS FIEF BY RIGHT OF INHERITANCE. IT IS NONE OF THE KING'S BUSINESS!"*

1593   © King Features Syndicate, Inc. 1967. World rights reserved   8-20

"WE ARRIVE AT A CONVENIENT TIME," ANSWERS VAL CALMLY, *"FOR I SEE YOU HAVE ALL THE PAPERS AT HAND. WE WILL LEAVE AS SOON AS YOUR CLAIM IS JUSTIFIED."*

BALA HAD BEEN TAUGHT TO ADMIRE SUCH MEN AS SLIGOL, MEN OF STRENGTH WHO TOOK WHAT THEY WANTED. WHY THEN DOES SLIGOL LOOK SUCH A TAWDRY THING COMPARED WITH PRINCE VALIANT, WHO FOOLISHLY RISKS HIS LIFE FOR NOTHING?

NEXT WEEK— *Sligol's Plan*

Prince Valiant

BY HAROLD R FOSTER

Our Story: PRINCE VALIANT SAYS: "SIR SLIGOL, YOU HAVE LAID CLAIM TO WICKWAIN AND ALL ITS WIDE LANDS, AND YOUR CLAIM SEEMS VALID. NOW SUMMON THE LADY CLIVE THAT WE MAY HEAR HER SIDE."

"I WILL NOT HAVE WOMEN INTERFERING IN MY BUSINESS!" SHOUTS SLIGOL. "THEY GET HYSTERICAL, THEY WEEP AND WILL NOT LISTEN TO LOGIC. I HAVE CONFINED THEM TO THE SOLARIUM."

VAL TURNS TO NOEL. "GO ESCORT THE LADIES HITHER. SHOULD ANYONE HESITATE TO UNLOCK DOORS ON YOUR REQUEST YOU ARE TO SAY, 'IT IS ORDERED BY THE KING'S DEPUTY!'"

LADY CLIVE, PROUD AND ERECT, ENTERS ON THE ARM OF HER NEPHEW, NOEL. WITH HER IS HER DAUGHTER, MEG, THICKSET, A SNUB NOSE AND RED HAIR. THEY ARE FOLLOWED BY SLIGOL'S SON, A SALLOW-FACED YOUTH WITH THICK LIPS AND DARK EYES THAT FOLLOW MEG'S EVERY MOVE.

THERE IS BUT ONE CHAIR IN THE ROOM AND IN THAT SLIGOL SITS AT EASE, LETTING THE LADIES STAND. VAL POINTS TO THE BENCHES ON WHICH THE GUARDS SIT. "BRING ONE OF THOSE HERE," HE ORDERS. AT A SIGN FROM SLIGOL THE GUARDS KEEP THEIR PLACES. "IS THIS THE ONE YOU WANT, SIR VALIANT?" ASKS BALA.

"THERE IS NOT ONE DROP OF CLIVE BLOOD IN SLIGOL'S VEINS. HIS CLAIM IS FALSE. THE CLOSEST MALE RELATIVE, NOEL, IS EXECUTOR. WHEN MEG MARRIES SHE AND HER HUSBAND HOLD WICKWAIN IN TRUST FOR THEIR SON, SHOULD THEY BE SO FORTUNATE AS TO HAVE ONE. HE WILL INHERIT ALL LANDS AND TITLE, SO SAYS MY LATE HUSBAND'S WILL."

HAL FOSTER

"WHAT DID I TELL YOU!" ROARS SLIGOL. "BRING WOMEN INTO MAN'S AFFAIRS AND THEY ONLY MESS THINGS UP. SUCH NONSENSE. THERE IS NO WILL."
"HOWEVER, I HAVE SOLVED THE PROBLEM. I SHALL WED THE LADY CLIVE, AND MY SON, FONDE, WILL MARRY MEG."

NEXT WEEK— **The Burned Document**

8-27

1594

Our Story: WITH WHAT HE THOUGHT WAS A MASTER STROKE, SLIGOL SETTLED THE QUESTION OF HERITAGE OF THE FIEF; HE WOULD MARRY EARL CLIVE'S WIDOW AND HIS SON WOULD MARRY MEG, HER DAUGHTER. A GOOD PLAN, FOR SLIGOL WOULD THEN BE COMPLETE MASTER OF WICKWAIN.

"I WOULD RATHER BE A SCULLERY MAID THAN YOUR WIFE," SAYS LADY CLIVE IN A VOICE FILLED WITH CONTEMPT.
"AND SO YOU SHALL," SLIGOL RETORTS, "UNTIL YOUR BACK BREAKS AND YOUR FINGERS BLEED."

MEG TOO IS QUITE DEFINITE. "THE FIRST TIME YOU PUT YOUR COLD, FURTIVE HANDS ON ME I'LL SCRATCH YOUR EYES OUT!" FONDE STILL SMILES, BUT NOW THERE IS CRUELTY AS WELL AS DESIRE IN THAT SMILE.

LADY CLIVE INSISTS THERE IS A WILL AND VAL RETURNS TO SEARCH AMONG THE DOCUMENTS FOR IT. SLIGOL SITS BEHIND THE TABLE, A CHARCOAL BRAZIER AT HIS SIDE TO SOFTEN THE AUTUMN CHILL.... AND TO BURN UNWANTED DOCUMENTS. VAL PLUCKS SOME UNBURNED ONES OFF AND STAMPS OUT THE FLAMES.

"THIS LOOKS LIKE THE CHARRED REMAINS OF A WILL." NOEL AGREES: "IT DOES LOOK LIKE PART OF MY UNCLE'S WILL. THERE ARE THE SIGNATURES OF THREE WITNESSES. ONE IS LORD LAMORIC'S, WHO IS DEAD. SIR DONIAN IS IN CORNWALL AND CANNOT BE REACHED, BUT SIR GRENWOLD IS A NEIGHBOR AND CAN BE FETCHED BY THE MORROW."

NOEL ARMS AND MOUNTS. "IF I RIDE ALL NIGHT I CAN REACH SIR GRENWOLD'S FIEF AT DAWN AND RETURN LATE TOMORROW."

1595 © King Features Syndicate, Inc. 1967. World rights reserved. 9-3

SLIGOL IS DESPERATE. HE SENDS TWO OF HIS ARMED GUARDS IN PURSUIT. HE INTENDS THAT WICKWAIN WILL BE HIS, AND A FEW MURDERS HERE AND THERE ARE ONLY INCIDENTAL.

BUT THE PURSUERS ARE THEMSELVES PURSUED! AND ONCE AGAIN THE DRAWBRIDGE SHAKES UNDER POUNDING HOOFS THAT FADE AWAY INTO THE NIGHT AS THE CLOAK OF DARKNESS COVERS A DESPERATE RACE.
NEXT WEEK—Bala to the Rescue

Prince Valiant

IN THE DAYS OF KING ARTHUR

BY Harold R Foster

Our Story: WHEN PRINCE VALIANT RODE OFF INTO THE NIGHT ON A SECRET MISSION HE DID NOT INFORM BALA, THINKING HIM TO BE UNTRUSTWORTHY AND A BIT STUPID. NOW BALA GOES IN SEARCH OF HIS LEADER.

AS HE ENTERS VAL'S ROOM SLIGOL IS SURPRISED IN THE ACT OF PAWING THROUGH VAL'S THINGS, SEARCHING FOR THE REMAINING HALF OF EARL CLIVE'S WILL.
BALA LOOKS AT HIM COLDLY. "GET OUT!" HE SAYS.

SLIGOL EXPLAINS, BLUSTERS AND THREATENS. "GET OUT!" REPEATS BALA, AND THE LOOK ON HIS FACE MAKES IT SEEM UNWISE TO TARRY ANY LONGER.

IN THE ABSENCE OF PRINCE VALIANT THERE IS NO ONE TO RESTRAIN FONDE. BALA FINDS HIM STRUGGLING WITH MEG AND HURLS HIM INTO A CORNER WHERE HE LIES SCREAMING FOR THE GUARDS.

BALA LOVES TO FIGHT, AND NOW HE GETS HIS WISH IN FULL MEASURE. THREE COME TO THE ATTACK AND SOON THERE ARE ONLY TWO, AND THESE TWO ARE LOSING THEIR ENTHUSIASM.

SLIGOL SEES HIS CHANCE TO REGAIN THE CASTLE. HE ORDERS THE GATES CLOSED SO NOEL AND VAL WILL BE SHUT OUT, AND CALLS ON THE REST OF HIS MEN TO SETTLE WITH BALA.

NOW THE ODDS ARE OVERWHELMING, BUT SOME HELP COMES FROM AN UNEXPECTED QUARTER. MEG PICKS UP A SPEAR AND, EYES BLAZING, THRUSTS MANFULLY INTO THE PRESS.

NEXT WEEK- The Secret Way

9-10

1596